Lotus
Illustrated
DICTIONARY
of
CIVIL
ENGINEERING

Complied and Edited by:
M.L. Sharman

Lotus PRESS

4735/22, Prakash Deep Building
Ansari Road, Darya Ganj,
New Delhi-110002

Lotus Illustrated
DICTIONARY
of

CIVIL ENGINEERING

© Lotus Press: 2013

ISBN 81 89093 22 3

Published by:
Lotus Press : Publishers & Distributors
Unit No. 220, 2nd Floor, 4735/22,
Prakash Deep Building, Ansari Road, Darya Ganj,
New Delhi- 110002, Ph.: 32903912, 23280047, 09811838000
• E-mail : lotus_press@sify.com, www.lotuspress.co.in

*Printed at : **Afcons Enterprises**, New Delhi*

PREFACE

Civil Engineering is a branch of engineering that embraces expert practices which work towards creating, maintaining and operating the social, commercial, and industrial infrastructure that sustains a modern society. Such infrastructure includes all building construction, roads, railways, canals, airports, harbours, docks, water supply, drainage, flood and erosion control, bridges, tunnels, pipelines, dams, irrigation systems, electricity generation, and industrial facilities.

This branch of engineering uses mathematics, physics, mechanics and the properties of materials in order to provide cost-effective solutions to building problems. This is brought about by combining the standard and best available expertise, labour and materials, keeping in mind the time, cost, hazards and social responsibility.

Historically, military engineers were responsible for the design and construction of roads, fortifications, bridges, and the destruction of enemy facilities by tunnelling and explosives. Eventually, this expertise entered the civilian domain, thereby becoming the profession of the civil engineer, which has nowadays become a competitive and quite sought after profession.

The dictionary is made with the intent of creating a ready to use repertoire of the terms used in this branch of engineering. It takes into account almost all the terms that are used as a part and parcel of the subject. The description of each term is kept simple by using a lucid and clear language. The explanation is also supported by examples and pictures to provide the readers with an enriching and healthy learning experience.

■ **0.2% floodplain**

an area of land that has a 0.2% chance of being inundated by flood waters from a bayou or creek in a given year.

■ **0.2% rainfall**

an amount of rain that has a 0.2% chance of falling during a certain duration, typically 24 hours, at a given location during a given year.

■ **1% floodplain**

also known as the Base Flood, it is an area of land that has a 1% chance of being inundated by flood waters from a bayou or creek in a given year.

■ **1% rainfall**

an amount of rain that has a 1% chance of falling during a certain duration, typically 24 hours, at a given location during a given year.

■ **a**

symbol for area of a cross section and fatigue stress ratio.
$a = f/s$
where f is the force perpendicular to the bond line and s is the surface area of the bond.

■ **a glass**

an early reinforcing glass fibre with a tensile strength 3.1 GPA, tensile modulus 72 GPA, specific tensile strength 1.26 GPA and specific modulus of 29 GPA. The symbol a was for alkali glass. Now superseded by e glass.

■ **a/c**

abbreviation for advanced composite.

■ **aa**

abbreviation for
1. alkyl alcohol
2. aluminium association
3. arithmetical average.

■ **abandoned water right**

A water right, which was not put to beneficial use for a number of years, generally five to seven years.

■ **abandoned well**

a well, which is no longer used. In many places, abandoned wells must be filled with cement or concrete grout to prevent pollution of ground water bodies.

■ **a-basis**

the value above which at least 99% of all test values are expected to fall, with a confidence level of 95% in published mechanical property values.

■ **abbe refractometer**

common form of refractometer used for determining the refractive index of liquids. Good accuracy is attainable in the range of 1.3 to 1.7, readings being given to the fourth decimal place. The prisms, which constitute the most important part of the instrument, and hence the liquid held between their faces, are capable of being maintained accurately at the temperature of the determination. With the use of special liquids to form an optical seal to the prisms and a special technique of viewing, it is also used for determining the refractive index of solids, such as plastics cast in sheets, with polished surfaces and edges.

■ ABFA

abbreviation for Azobisfor-mamide.

■ abherent

a coating or film applied to one surface to prevent or reduce its adhesion to another surface brought into intimate contact with it. Abherent applied to plastic films are often called anti-blocking agents. Those applied to moulds, calendar rolls and the like are also known as release agent, parting agent, or abhesive.

■ abhesive

see **abherent**.

■ abietates

esters or salts of abietic acid, a principal constituent of ordinary rosin from which the products of commerce are derived, no attempt being made to separate abietic acid from the other acids which rosin is likely to contain. Esters of rosin are described as abietates and include the methyl, ethyl and benzyl derivatives, which are used chiefly as plasticisers.

■ abietic acid

product consisting chiefly of rosin acids in substantially pure form, separated from rosin or tall oil, in which abietic acid and its isomers are the principal components.

■ abl bottle

an internal pressure test vessel about 18 inches in diameter and 24 inches long, used to determine the quality and properties of the filament wound material used to fabricate the vessel.

■ ablation

an orderly heat and mass transfer process in which a large amount of thermal energy is expended by sacrificial loss of surface region material. The heat input from the environment is absorbed, dissipated, blocked and generated by numerous mechanisms. The energy adsorption processes take place automatically and simultaneously, serve to control the surface temperature, and greatly restrict the flow of heat into the substrate interior.

■ ablative coatings

thick materials used for missiles and re-entry rockets which absorb heat and are designed to char and sacrifice themselves while protecting the metal substrate underneath.

■ ablative material

a term applied to any polymer or resin with low thermal conductivity which pyrolyses layer-by-layer when its surface is heated, leaving a heat-resisting layer of charred material which eventually breaks away to expose virgin material. Ablative plastics are used on nose cones of projectiles, re-entry rockets and space vehicles to isolate and protect them from hyperthermal effects of the environment.

■ aboveground storage tank

a non- vehicular device (including any associated piping that is made of non- earthen materials) located on or above the surface of the ground, or on or above the surface of the floor of a structure below the ground, such as mineworking, basement or vault; and designed to contain an accumulation of petroleum products.

■ **abrading equipment**

a type of equipment which fires a gas propelled stream of finely graded abrasive particles through a precise nozzle against a work surface.

■ **abrasiometer**

one of the many devices used to test abrasion of a coating by using an air blast to drive an abrasive against the test film, or by rotating a film submerged in an abrasive, or by simply dropping a stream of abrasive onto the film.

■ **abrasion**

wear or removal of the surface of a solid material as a result of relative movement of other solid bofies in contact with it

■ **abrasion cycle**

number of abrading revolutions to which a specimen is subjected in an abrasion test such as with a taber abrader.

■ **abrasion machine**

a laboratory device for determining abrasive resistance.

■ **abrasion resistance**

1. the ability of a construction element, such as a floor, pavement, roof or coating to resist degradation due to mechanical wear such as foot or wheel traffic and wind blown particles which tend to progressively remove materials from its surface.

2. the ability of a material to withstand mechanical action such as rubbing, scraping, or erosion, that tends progressively to remove material from its surface. Such an ability helps to maintain the material's original appearance and structure.

■ **abrasive**

any agent which, by a process of grinding down, tends to remove material from a surface.

■ **abrasive cutoff**

a grinding process employing a thin, bonded abrasive wheel for cutting.

■ **abrasive finishing**

a method of removing flash, marks and rough edges from plastic articles by means of abrasive belts, disks, or wheels. The process is usually employed on large rigid or semi-rigid products with intricate surfaces which cannot be treated by tumbling or other more efficient de-flashing methods.

■ **abrasive flow machining**

a finishing process for holes and inaccessible areas using an extruded semisolid abrasive media.

■ **abrasive media**

moderately to extremely hard materials, usually in a fine or very fine particulate form, used in abrasive blasting to remove surface contaminants or to grind and polish samples to the desired thickness or finish. Examples of moderately hard abrasive media are sand, iron shot, crushed iron slag, glass beads or ground nut shells.

Examples of extremely hard abrasive media are industrial diamonds.

■ **abrasive wear**

hard particles or protuberances forced against and moving along a solid surface.

■ **abrasive wire band sawing**

a method of band sawing employing a small diameter wire with diamond or other abrasive bonded to the cutting blade.

■ **abrasiveness**

the property of a material to remove matter when scratching or grinding another material.

■ **ABS resins**

abbreviation for Acrylonitrile-Butadiene-Styrene. A family of thermoplastics or terpolymers based on acrylonitrile, butadiene and styrene combined by a variety of methods involving polymerksation, graft copolymerisation, physical mixtures and combinations thereof. The standard grades are rigid, hard and tough but not brittle, and possess good impact strength, heat resistance, low temperature properties, chemical resistance and electrical properties.

■ **absolute**

describes measurements in terms of fundamentally defined units.

■ **absolute accuracy**

the measurement of exactness from a specified reference point.

■ **absolute alcohol**

pure anhydrous ethyl alcohol (ethanol). The term is used to distinguish it from the several varieties of alcohol which are available, and which contain varying amounts of water and/or other impurities, or denaturants.

■ **absolute dimension**

one that is expressed relative to the origin of a coordinate axis, but not necessarily coinciding with the absolute zero point.

■ **absolute pressure**

a pressure scale with the zero point at a perfect vacuum. The sum of atmospheric and gauge pressure.

■ **absolute reflectance**

reflectance measured relative to the perfect diffuser.

■ **absolute specific gravity**

the ratio of the weight of a given volume of a substance to that of an equal volume of water at the same temperature, as determined by an apparatus which provides correction for the effects of air buoyancy.

■ **absorb**

To take in. Many things absorb water.

■ **absorbance**

logarithm of the reciprocal of spectral internal transmittance.

■ **absorbant**

material in which absorption occurs.

■ **absorbed water**

mechanically held water in a porous material (as concrete, soil mass, aggregates) and having physical properties not substantially different from ordinary water at the same temperature and pressure.

■ **absorbent filters**

a filter medium that entraps contaminants and holds it by mechanical means.

■ **absorptance**

the ratio of radiant energy absorbed to total incident radiant energy.

■ **absorption**

1. the weight of water a solid (such as a brick unit) absorbs, when immersed in either cold or boiling water for a stated length of time. Expressed as a percentage of the weight of the dry unit for masonry.
2. process in which molecules are taken up by a liquid or solid and distributed throughout its body; compare with **adsorption**.
3. the penetration of a substance into the mass of another substance by molecular or chemical action.
4. the process whereby energy is dissipated within a specimen placed in a field of radiation energy.
5. decrease in directional transmittance of incident radiation, resulting in a modification or conversion of the radiant energy into heat, for example. Light incident on a specimen may be partially reflected, partially transmitted, or partially absorbed. Not to be confused with adsorption, a purely surface phenomenon.

■ **absorption band**

a region of the absorption spectrum in which the absorption is strong.

■ **absorption coefficient**

absorption of radiant energy for a unit concentration through a unit path length for a specified wavelength and angle of incidence and viewing.

■ **absorption field**

area through which septic tank effluent discharges (through leaching or seepage) into the surrounding ground. It comprises of a series of perforated pipes laid in shallow trenches backfilled with a pre-designed arrangement of sand and gravel.

■ **absorption rate**

absorption expressed as function of time.

■ **absorption spectro-photometry**

measurement of the amount of radiant energy absorbed as a function of wavelength or frequency. Ultra-violet radiant energy can be employed as the source of incident radiant energy, and it has been found that certain groupings of atoms in organic compounds influence the intensity and location of the absorption bands in the ultimate spectrum.

■ **abut**

to adjoin at an end, to be contiguous.

■ **abutment**

substructure unit supporting the ends of a bridge and, usually, retaining the approach embankment.

■ **accelerated ageing**

any set of conditions designed to produce in a short time the results obtained under normal conditions of ageing. In an accelerated ageing test, the usual factors considered are heat, light, or oxygen, either separately or combined. Also known as accelerated life.

■ **accelerated corrosion test**

a test method designed to simulate, in a short time span, the destructive action of corrosion under normal long-term service conditions.

■ **accelerated test**

a test procedure in which conditions are intensified to reduce the time required to obtain a deteriorating effect similar to one resulting from normal service conditions.

■ **accelerated weathering**

1. a test designed to simulate the deteriorating effect of natural outdoor weathering, with controlled, intensified and accelerated processes.
2. tests designed to simulate, but at the same time to intensify and hasten, the destructive action of natural outdoor weathering on a material. They involve the exposure of a material to artificially produced components of natural weather, e.g., light, heat, cold, water vapour and rain, which are arranged and repeated in a given cycle.

■ **accelerated weathering machine**

device intended to accelerate the deterioration of coatings by exposing them to controlled sources of radiant energy, heat, water or other factors that may be introduced. Also known as weather meter.

■ **acceleration coefficient**

a dimensionless coefficient, as a fraction of the acceleration of gravity, used to describe the anticipated ground motion due to seismic forces.

■ **accelerator**

1. substance used in small proportions to increase the speed of a chemical reaction. Accelerators are often used in the paint industry to speed up drying.
2. a substance used in small proportions which hastens a reaction, usually by acting in conjunction with a catalyst or a curing agent. An accelerator is sometimes used in the polymerisation of thermoplastics, but is used most widely in curing systems for thermosets.

■ **acceptable quality level**

the maximum percent defective that, for purposes of sampling inspection, can be considered satisfactory as the process average.

■ **acceptance**

a test that determines conformance of a product to design specifications as a basis for acceptance.

■ **acceptance level**

a test level above or below which test specimens are acceptable, as contrasted to a rejection level.

■ **acceptance number**

the maximum number of defects in a sample that will permit acceptance of the inspection lot.

■ **accretion**

increase in size of a mass by a process of external additions.

■ **accumulator**

1. in blow moulding, an auxiliary ram extruder used to provide fast parson delivery. The accumulator cylinder is filled with plasticated melt from the main extruder between parson deliveries or 'shots', and stores this melt until the plunger is required to deliver the next parson.
2. a device for conserving energy in hydraulic systems of moulding equipment.

■ **accuracy**

1. the quality or freedom from mistake or error, the concept of exactness, or the extent to which the result of a calculation or a measurement approaches the true value of the actual parameter.

2. the degree of conformity or agreement of a measured or calculated value to some recognised standard or specified value.

■ **acetal**

a colourless, inflammable, volatile liquid used as a solvent.

■ **acetal copolymer resins**

a family of highly crystalline thermoplastics prepared by copolymerising trioxane with small amounts of a comonomer which randomly distributes carbon-carbon bonds in the polymer chain. These bonds, as well as hydroxy ethyl terminal units, give the acetal copolymers a high degree of thermal stability and resistance to strong alkaline environments.

■ **acetal resins**

rigid engineering thermoplastics produced by the addition polymerisation of aldehydes through the carbonyl function, yielding unbranched polyoxymethylene chains of great length. Among the strongest and stiffest of all thermoplastics, the acetal resins are characterised by good fatigue life, resilience, low moisture sensitivity, high solvent and chemical resistance, and good electrical properties. They can be glass reinforced and may be processed by conventional injection moulding and extrusion techniques, and fabricated by welding methods used for other plastics. Also known as polyformaldehyde and polyoxymethylenes.

■ acetaldehyde

a liquid synthesised by the hydration of acetylene, the oxidation or dehydrogenation of ethyl alcohol, or the oxidation of saturated hydrocarbons or ethylene. It is a highly reactive intermediate used for the production of thermosetting resins and with polyvinyl alcohol to form polyvinyl acetal resins. Also known as ethanol, ethyl aldehyde and acetic aldehyde.

■ acetaldehyde resin

product of the auto-condensation of acetaldehyde.

■ acetate fibres

fibres made by partially acetylating cellulose.

■ acetates

1. metallic salts derived from acetic acid by interaction of the metallic oxide, hydroxide, or carbonate with the acid; or the esters derived by interaction of alcohols with acetic acid which include the common esters of ethyl, propyl, isopropyl, butyl and amyl acetates, etc.
2. a generic name for cellulose acetate plastics, particularly for fibres thereof. When at least 92% of the hydroxyl groups are acetylated, the term triacetate may be used as the generic name of the fibre.
3. a compound containing the acetate group, CH_3COO.

■ acetic acid–CH_3COOH

monobasic colourless liquid used in the manufacture of metallic acetates for the production of driers, and in the manufacture of acetate esters employed as solvents or plasticisers. Also known as ethanoic acid and vinegar acid.

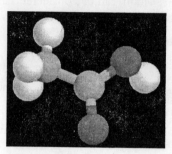

■ acetic anhydride

the acid anhydride of acetic acid used in the manufacture of many raw materials and intermediates.

■ acetone

a low-boiling, ketone solvent, which has a flashpoint well below the freezing point of water: -9°c (15°f). Also known as dimethyl ketone.

■ acetone extraction

the amount of acetone-soluble material that can be extracted from a material; is an indication of the degree of cure.

■ acetonyl acetone

a diketonic solvent.

■ acetyl cyclohexane sulphonyl peroxide

a polymerisation initiator, often used in conjunction with a dicarbonate such as di-sec-butyl peroxy dicarbonate.

■ acetyl groups

the characteristic acetic acid radical (CH_3CO).

■ **acetyl number**

number of milligrams of potassium hydroxide required to neutralise the acetic acid set free from 1 gram of acetylated compound when the latter is subjected to hydrolysis.

■ **acetyl peroxide**

a resin catalyst which is also known as di-acetyl peroxide.

■ **acetyl triallyl citrate**

a cross-linking agent for polyesters.

■ **acetylation**

the substitution of an acetyl radical for an active hydrogen. A reaction involving the replacement of the hydrogen atom of an hydroxyl group with an acetyl radical (CH_3CO) to yield a specific ester, the acetate. Acetic anhydride is commonly used as an acetylating agent reacting with free hydroxyl groups.

■ **acetylene**

a colourless gas derived by reacting water with calcium carbide, or by cracking petroleum hydrocarbons. An important intermediate in the production of vinyl chloride, acrylonitrile, etc. Also known as ethyne.

■ **acetylene black**

a particularly pure form of graphitic, carbon black pigment, made by the controlled combustion of acetylene in air under pressure. It is used as a filler in plastics to impart electrical conductivity.

■ **acid**

1. chemical substance that yields hydrogen ions (H^+) when dissolved in water. This hydrogen may be replaced by metals with the formation of salts.
2. a solution of pH less than 7.0 at 25 degrees C (pH=5.5-7 signifies mild acidity).
3. compounds characterised by ionisable hydrogen atoms. With organic acids or carboxylic acids the ionisable hydrogen atom is directly attached through an oxygen atom, to a carbon atom, e.g., acetic acid CH_3COOH. The inorganic acids, or mineral acids, include HCL, HNO_3, H_2SO_4, H_3PO_4, etc.

■ **acid curing**

process of curing or hardening resins through the use of acid catalysts.

■ **acid embrittlement**

form of hydrogen embrittlement that may be induced in some metals by acid treatment or other acid exposure.

■ **acid etch**

to clean or alter a surface using acid.

■ **acid groups**

functional groups such as carboxyl groups having the properties of acids.

■ **acid mine waste**

one of the principal pollutants arising from mining operations. Acid water forms when water contacts certain types of exposed mine wastes and ores.

■ **acid number**

1. the quantity of base, expressed in milligrams of potassium hy-

droxide, that is required to neutralise the acidic constituents in one gram of sample. See **neutralisation number**.
2. the measure of free acid content of a substance. It is expressed as the number of milligrams of KOH neutralised by the free acid present in one gram of the substance. This value is sometimes used in connection with the end-group method of determining the molecular weight of polyesters. It is also used in evaluating plasticisers, in which acid values should be as low as possible.

■ **acid rain**

the acidic rainfall, which results when rain combines with Sulphur oxides emissions from combustion of fossil fuels (coal).

■ **acid resistance**

ability of materials to resist attack by acids. Most plastics have a high degree of acid resistance.

■ **acid-etch tube**

a glass tube charged with dilute hydrofluoric acid. Used to measure inclination: after being left in a borehole for 20 to 30 min, the inclination will be indicated by the angle of etch line on the tube. This method is called 'acid-dip survey'.

■ **acidimeter**

an apparatus or standard solution used to determine the amount of acid in a sample.

■ **acidity**

measure of free acid present.

■ **acidolysis**

the process of reacting an acid with an ester or an ester exchange.

■ **acoustic emission testing**

a non-destructive test method for determining or monitoring material or structural integrity based on the release of energy detectable by analysis of the emission frequency and amplitude.

■ **acoustical board**

a low-density, structural, insulating, sound-absorbing board—having a fissured, felted-fibre, slotted or perforated surface pattern provided to reduce sound reflection. Usually supplied for use in the form of tiles.

■ **acoustical material**

any material considered in terms of its acoustical properties. Commonly, and especially, a material designed to absorb sound.

■ **acre-foot**

the amount of water required to cover one acre to a depth of one foot. An acre-foot equals 326,851 gallons, or 43,560 cubic feet.

■ **acrolein**

a liquid derived from the oxidation of allyl alcohol or propylene, used as an intermediate in the production of polyester resins and polyurethanes. Also known as acrylic aldehyde and propenal.

■ **acrylamide**

a crystalline solid acid amide, capable of polymerisation or copolymerisation.

■ **acrylates**

1. acrylic acid esters.
2. metallic salts of acrylic acid.

■ **acrylic**

1. thermoplastic with reasonable optical clarity, plus good weather and shatter resistance.
2. one of the resins present in latex paints. It serves as bonding agent for the other ingredients.
3. a synthetic resin from acrylic acid or a derivative thereof. Clarity is the property for which the resin is known.

■ **acrylic acid**

a colourless, unsaturated acid which polymerises readily. The homopolymer is not often used except as a textile sizing agent, but esters of acrylic acid are widely used in the production of acrylic resins. Also known as propenoic acid.

■ **acrylic esters**

esters of acrylic or methacrylic acid or of their structural derivatives which vary from soft, elastic, film-forming materials to hard plastics. Readily polymerised as homopolymers or copolymers with many other monomers, contributing to improved resistance to heat, light and weathering. They serve as plasticisers during processing, then polymerise during cure to impart hardness to the finished article. Also known as acryl esters.

■ **acrylic fibre**

generic name for a manufactured fibre in which the fibre-forming material is any long chain synthetic polymer composed of at least 85 % by weight of acrylonitrile units $CH_2CH(CN)$.

■ **acrylic latex**

an aqueous dispersion of acrylic resins in latex paints.

■ **acrylic plastics**

thermoplastic or thermosetting polymers or copolymers of acrylic acid, methacrylic acid, esters of these acids, or acrylonitrile, sometimes modified with nonacrylic monomers such as the **ABS** group. Glass fibres reinforced composites of acrylic resins can be processed by injection moulding, vacuum forming and compression moulding. A pultruded graphite reinforced acrylic IPN has been reported with a flexural strength of 1601 VS 1794 MPA (233 VS 260 KSI) for an epoxy system with similar processing.

■ **acrylic resins**

polymers of acrylic or methacrylic esters, sometimes modified with nonacrylic monomers such as the ABS group. The acrylates may be methyl, ethyl, butyl or 2-ethylhexyl. Usual methacrylates are methyl, ethyl, butyl, laural and stearyl. The resins may be in the form of moulding powders or casting syrups, and are noted for their exceptional clarity and optical properties. Acrylics are widely used in lighting fixtures because they are slow burning or may be made self-extinguishing, and do not produce harmful smoke or gases in the presence of flame.

■ acrylonitrile

a monomer that is most useful in copolymers. Several of its copolymers with styrene are tougher than polystyrene. It is also used as a synthetic fibre and as a chemical intermediate. Also known as propenenitrile and vinyl cyanide.

■ acrylonitrile-butadiene-styrene

a family of three-polymer engineering thermoplastics. Acrylonitrile and styrene liquids, and butadiene gas are polymerised together in a variety of ratios to produce desired electrical properties, chemical resistance, and dimensional stability.

■ acrylonitrile-styrene co-polymers

a series of copolymers which have the transparency of polystyrene, but with improved stress cracking and solvent resistance.

■ activate

to put into a state of increased chemical activity.

■ activating

a treatment which renders non-conductive material receptive to electroless deposition.

■ activation

1. the changing of a passive metal surface to a chemically active state. Contrast with **passivation.**
2. the treatment of a substance by heat, radiation, or a chemical reagent to produce a more rapid physical and/or chemical change.

■ activator

1. the activation agent of metal surface.
2. the curing agent of a two component product such as a coating system or an adhesive.
3. an additive used in a small proportion to promote the curing of matrix resins and reduce curing time, an accelerator.

■ active

state in which a metal tends to corrode; opposite of passive or noble.

■ active earth pressure

horizontal push from earth on a retaining wall.

■ active oxygen

a measure of the oxidising power of a substance expressed in terms of oxygen with a gram-equivalent weight of 8.00.

■ active solar heating

a space heating system in which heat from the sun is absorbed by collectors and transferred by pumps or fans to a storage unit for later use or to the house interior directly. Controls regulating the operation are needed.

■ active solar water heater

a water heating system in which heat from the sun is absorbed by collectors and transferred by pumps to a storage unit. The heated fluid in the storage unit conveys its heat to the domestic hot water of the house through a heat exchanger. Controls regulating the operation are needed.

■ **activity, catalyst**

the measure of the rate of a specific catalytic reaction.

■ **ACTP**

abbreviation for Advanced-Composite Thermoplastics.

■ **actuators**

devices that control the movement of mechanical action of a machine indirectly rather than directly or by hand. They can perform linear or rotary motions, and are usually motivated by means of pneumatic or hydraulic cylinders.

■ **acyl groups**

radicals derived from carboxylic acids by removal of an OH group.

■ **acylation**

formation or introduction of an acyl radical in or into an organic compound.

■ **ADA**

abbreviation for Adipic Acid.

■ **Adams and Walrath test**

a mechanical test method for composites employing double-cantilever beam type loading.

■ **adaptive control system**

a system that modifies its control algorithm as the system's operating conditions change so that optimal performance can be achieved.

■ **addition polymer**

polymer made by addition polymerisation.

■ **addition polymerisation or additive**

a chemical reaction in which simple molecules (monomers) are added to each other to form long-chain molecules (polymers) without by-products. The molecules of the monomer join together to form a polymeric product in which the molecular formula of the repeating unit is identical with that of the monomer. The molecular weight of the polymer so formed is thus the total of the molecular weights of all of the combined monomer units.

■ **adduct**

a chemical addition product, such as the cyclic product of the addition of a diene with another unsaturated compound (as maleic anhydride).

■ **adduct curing agent**

a cross-linking agent.

■ **adhere**

to cause two surfaces to be held together by adhesion, typically with asphalt or roofing cements in built-up roofing and with contact cements in some single-ply membranes.

■ **adherence**

the degree of adhesion of two surfaces.

■ **adherometer**

an instrument which measures the strength of an adhesive bond.

■ **adhesion**

1. the degree of attachment between two or more bodies during their service life, such as a paint film to the underlying material to which it is in contact (substrate) or the ability of a roofing membrane to remain attached to the substrate or to itself.
2. the state in which two surfaces are held together by interfacial forces which may consist of valence forces or interlocking action or both.

■ **adhesion agent**

a substance used for the purpose of improving the adhesion between a bituminous binder and the aggregate. The term generally refers to adhesion in the presence of water.

■ **adhesion failure**

the separation of two bonded surfaces at an interface by the application of force.

■ **adhesion promoter**

a substance which is applied to a substrate to improve the adhesion of a coating to the substrate. Typical adhesion promoters are based on silanes and silicones with hydrolysable groups on one end of their molecules which react with moisture to yield silanol groups, which in turn react with or adsorb inorganic surfaces to enable strong bonds to be made. At the other ends of the molecules are reactive, but non-hydrolysable groups that are compatible with resin formulations

■ **adhesion strength**

the force required to cause a separation of two bonded surfaces.

■ **adhesion, mechanical**

adhesion between surfaces in which the adhesive holds the pans together by interlocking action.

■ **adhesion, specific**

adhesion between surfaces which are held together by valence forces of the same type as those which promote cohesion.

■ **adhesive**

substance capable of holding materials together by surface attachment. Adhesive types include: a monomer of at least one of the polymers to be joined, catalysed to produce a bond by polymerisation; solvent cement which dissolves the plastics being joined, forming strong intermolecular bonds, and then evaporates; bonded adhesives or solvent solutions of resins, sometimes containing plasticisers, which dry at room temperature; and reactive adhesives or those containing partially polymerised resins, e.g., epoxies, polyesters or phenolics, which cure with the aid of catalysts to form a bond.

■ **adhesive dispersion**

two-phase adhesive system in which one phase is suspended in a liquid.

■ **adhesive film**

a thin, dry film of resin, usually a thermoset, used as an interleaf in the production of laminates such as plywood. Heat and pressure applied in the laminating process cause the film to bond both layers together.

■ **adhesive lock**

The adherence of surfaces due to weldment/fusion of asperity contact points/junctions or by increased surface contact area due to polishing.

■ **adhesive wear**

due to material transfer between two surfaces or loss from either surface between contacting bonded surfaces.

■ **adhesive, cold-setting**

adhesive which sets at temperatures below 20°C.

■ **adhesive, contact**

an adhesive which requires that for satisfactory bonding, the surfaces to be joined shall be no farther apart than about 0.1 mm.

■ **adhesive, edge jointing**

adhesive used to bond strips of veneer together by their edges in the formation of larger sheets.

■ **adhesive, heat activated**

a dry adhesive film that is rendered tacky or fluid by application of heat and/or pressure.

■ **adhesive, hot melt**

an adhesive applied in a molten state to form a bond on cooling.

■ **adhesive, hot-setting**

adhesive which requires a temperature at or above 100°C to cure.

■ **adhesive, intermediate temperature setting**

an adhesive that sets in the temperature range 31° to 99°C.

■ **adhesive, multiple layer**

an adhesive film that is usually supported with a different adhesive composition on each side for bonding dissimilar materials such as the core to face bond of a sandwich composite

■ **adhesive, pressure sensitive**

a viscoelastic, solvent-free, permanently-tacky material which adheres spontaneously to most solid surfaces with a slight application of pressure.

■ **adhesive, room temperature setting**

an adhesive that sets in the temperature range 20° to 30°C.

■ **adhesive, separate application**

an adhesive consisting of two parts. One part is applied to one adherent and another part to a second adherent, and the two are brought together to form a joint.

■ **adhesive, solvent**

an adhesive containing a volatile, organic liquid as the vehicle.

■ **adhesive, solvent activated**

dry adhesive rendered tacky just prior to use by application of a solvent.

■ **adhesive-assembly**

the process of joining two or more plastic parts other than flat sheets (for which the term laminating is used) by means of an adhesive.

■ **adhesive-bonded**

bonding is accomplished by adding an adhesive coating to the surface of the component, then joining and curing the adhesive.

■ **adhesiveness**

the property defined by the adhesion stress

■ **adiabatic**

denoting a process in which no heat is deliberately added or removed or there is no gain or loss of heat from the environment. Used somewhat incorrectly to describe the method of extrusion in which heat is developed from mechanical action of the screw to an extent sufficient to plastify the compound.

■ **admixture**

liquid or finely ground solid materials combined into a particular concrete, mortar or grout mix design in predetermined, minute, and very controlled quantities. The intended result is a major change in the behaviour of the resulting product.

■ **adsorbed water**

water held on surfaces of a material: in a soil or rock mass, this is water held by physico-chemical forces, having physical properties substantially different from absorbed water or chemically combined water, at the same temperature and pressure.

■ **adsorbent filters**

a filter medium primarily intended to hold soluble and insoluble con-

taminants on its surface by molecular adhesion.

■ **adsorption**

the adhesion of a substance to the surface of a solid or liquid. Adsorption is often used to extract pollutants by causing them to be attached to such adsorbents as activated carbon or silica gel. Hydrophobic, or water-repulsing adsorbents, are used to extract oil from waterways in oil spills.

■ **ADT**

Average Daily Traffic

■ **ADTT**

Average Daily Truck Traffic

■ **advance plans**

plans submitted to the region at approximately 75-90% completion for the purpose of a technical progress review. At this time, all excavation/embankment work should be defined and major structural components should be designed and detailed.

■ **advanced ceramic**

a value-added technical ceramic.

■ **aeration**

the process of bubbling air through a solution, sometimes cleaning water of impurities by exposure to the air.

■ **aerogel**

a microporous, transparent silicate foam used as a glasing cavity fill material, offering possible u-values below 0.10 btu/(h-sq ft-°f) or 0.56 w/(sq m-°c).

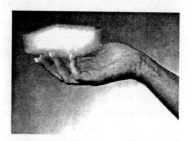

■ **age hardening**

process of hardening by ageing; in metals usually occurs after rapid cooling or cold working. It can be generally favourable (for concrete, mortar) or unfavourable (for metals, elastomers, etc.).

■ **aggregate**

1. a granular material either natural or processed from deposits of sand, gravel, rock etc.. Described as coarse aggregate or fine aggregate.
2. crushed stone, slag or waterworn gravel that comes in a wide range of sizes. Used to surface built-up roofs.

■ **ageing**

change in the properties of certain metals and alloys that occurs at ambient (or somewhat elevated) temperatures after hot working or a heat treatment (quench ageing in ferrous alloys, natural or artificial ageing in ferrous and nonferrous alloys) or after a cold-working operation (strain ageing). The change in properties does not involve a change in the chemical composition of the metal or alloy.

■ **agricultural by-products**

products developed in agriculture that are not the primary goal of the agricultural activity. Some of these are being used as building materials. An example is straw used to make wall panels, or as bales in a technique called straw bale construction.

■ **agricultural fibre**

agricultural fibres (i.e., cotton) are being introduced for use as insulation materials.

■ **air barrier**

intentionally designed and constructed barrier meant to prevent both the ex-filtration of indoor air to the outside and the infiltration of outdoor air into the building environment. This applies whether the air is humid or relatively dry. Air leakage will cause the deposition of moisture in both cavity and solid walls, as well as energy losses and rain infiltration.

■ **air cleaner fine test dust**

a naturally occurring material representative of contaminant associated with ingression-type systems. It is produced from natural Arizona road dust and it is processed, packaged, and distributed worldwide. Used for particle counter calibration, filter tests, and component contaminant sensitivity testing.

■ **air drying**

curing method of a film coating in which drying occurs by simple air exposure and without heat or the presence of a catalyst; the process of curing happens either by oxidation or by solvent evaporation.

■ air entrapment

intentional or accidental inclusion of air bubbles in materials such as concrete or liquid paint. Air bubbles present before curing tend to remain dispersed in the hardened material.

■ air impermeability

a major requirement of an air barrier is that it offer a high resistance to air flow. While absolute air impermeability may not be required, materials such as glass, sheet metal, gypsum board, cast-in-place concrete and a properly supported polyethylene sheet offer a much higher resistance to air flow than do more porous materials such as concrete blocks, fibre board sheathing, and expanded polystyrene insulation. A second major consideration is that individual panels be joined into an air-tight assembly. The joints between gypsum boards can be taped quickly and effectively, sheet metal panels can be lapped with tape, precast panels can be sealed with rope and sealants, etc.

■ air infiltration

the amount of air leaking in and out of a building through cracks in walls, windows and doors.

■ air leakage

air flow in and out of a building, which occurs under two conditions: there must be an opening in the building envelope and there must be an air pressure difference across the wall at that location. The opening need not be straight or direct through the wall: it can follow a convoluted path inside the wall. As for the pressure difference, it can result from one or combination of three possible causes: wind, stack effect, and fan pressurisation. Air leakage can cause a number of problems: spalling masonry, ice build-up under soffits, frozen pipes, condensation in cavities, rain leaks, high energy costs, and indoor humidity problems. The seeds for many of these pitfalls are sown during the design phase, largely because of major confusion concerning the function of the air and vapour barriers.

■ air leakage rating

a measure of the rate of infiltration around a window or skylight, or through a wall in the presence of a specific pressure difference. It is expressed in units of cubic feet per minute per square foot of window area (cfm/sq ft) or cubic feet per minute per foot of window perimeter length (cfm/ft). The lower an envelope component's air leakage rating, the better its air tightness.

■ air release valve

a check type valve having a movable closing element (e.g., a ball) with a density less than the host liquid. When the closure element is surrounded by air, the valve automatically opens and will close when it is surrounded by liquid.

air set cement

a cement that sets through loss of water.

air, standard

air at state conditions of 68° F, a pressure of 14.7 psi absolute, and a relative humidity of 35 percent.

airborne snow water equivalent measurement theory

a theory based on the fact that natural terrestrial gamma radiation is emitted from the potassium, uranium, and thorium radioisotopes in the upper eight inches of the soil. The radiation is sensed from low flying aircraft 500 feet above the ground. Water mass in the snow cover attenuates the terrestrial radiation signal. The difference between airborne radiation measurements made over bare ground and snow-covered ground can be used to calculate a mean aerial snow water equivalent value with a root mean square error of less than a half inch.

aircraft loading apron

a paved or unpaved surface for loading cargo aircraft; loading personnel for medical evacuation and transient aircraft operations; or providing an apron area for fuelling aircraft, arming and disarming aircraft weapons, loading and unloading ammunition, special handling or decontamination of chemical, biological, radiological (CBR) warfare items, and for special security operations.

aircraft maintenance parking apron

a paved or unpaved apron for parking fixed or rotary wing aircraft awaiting maintenance.

aircraft runway holding apron

a paved or unpaved surface providing an aircraft holding area accessible from a taxiway. It is located near the intersection of taxiways and ends of runways and is provided for pre-takeoff engine and instrument checks. For inventory purposes, only the prepared surface is included.

airdraulic

a component combining both an air and oil system; e.g., an intensifier using air as the driving medium and oil as the amplified pressure medium.

air-dried lumber

lumber that has been piled in yards or sheds for any length of time.

airfield pavements

prepared surfaces, other than runways and taxiways, where aircraft are parked or moved about the airfield. They are designed to support specific types of aircraft and to meet operational requirements such as maintenance and loading activities.

■ **airless spray**

a type of spraying system in which paint is atomised by using high hydraulic pressure, rather than compressed air.

■ **airway**

a space between roof insulation and roof boards for movement of air.

■ **ALCLAD**

composite material having an Aluminium Alloy Core Clad on one or both surfaces with a metallurgical bonded aluminium or aluminium alloy coating that is anodic to the core and thus electrochemically protects the core against corrosion.

■ **alcohol**

group of solvents including ethanol, methanol, and isopropyl; they tend to have relatively high evaporation rates and fairly low solvent strength.

■ **algae bloom**

a phenomenon- whereby excessive nutrients within a river, stream or lake causes an explosion of plant life, which results in the depletion of the oxygen in the water needed by fish and other aquatic life. Algae bloom is usually the result of urban runoff (of lawn fertilisers, etc.). The potential tragedy is that of a 'fish kill,' where the stream life dies in one mass extinction.

■ **algorithm**

a law, rule or procedure for solving a recurring mathematical problem.

■ **aliphatic hydrocarbons**

a class of organic solvents which are composed of open chains of carbon atoms. Aliphatics are relatively weak solvents. Mineral spirits and VM & P naphtha are aliphatic solvents.

■ **alkali**

an aqueous substance which has a pH value of 7-14; a base or caustic material.

■ **alkali metal**

any of the highly reactive metals (such as lithium, sodium, potassium, rubidium, caesium, and francium) found in the first column of the periodic table. They act as bases (form strongly alkaline hydroxides), hence the name.

■ **alkaline**

1. having a pH value of between 7 and 14
2. having properties of an alkali.
3. having a pH greater than 7.

■ **Alkali-Silica Reaction (ASR)**

reaction of alkalis in aggregate with various forms of poorly crystalline reactive silica: opal, chert, flint and chalcedony and also tridymite, crystoblite and volcanic glasses. Aggregate containing such materials (e.g., some cherty gravels) may cause deterioration of concrete when present in amounts of 1% to 5%. Concrete made of these aggregates is characterised by the early onset of a relatively rapid expansion. Cracking of structures is often observed within 10 years of construction.

■ **alkyd**

common term for oil based paints

■ **alkyd resin**

modified form of resins prepared by combining alcohol and fatty acids. Widely used in general purpose coatings such as laquer paints, varnishes, and metal finishes.

■ **alligatoring**

1. roofing or pavement defect characterised by randomised cracking of the surfacing bitumen, producing a pattern of cracks similar to an alligator's hide; these cracks may or may not extend through the whole thickness of the surfacing bitumen.
2. a characteristic of asphalt which occurs during the ageing process in which the loss of volatile oils and the oxidation brought about by solar radiation produces a pattern of cracks which resemble an alligator hide, because of the limited tolerance of asphalt to thermal expansion or contraction.
3. coarse checking pattern characterised by a slipping of the new paint coating over the old coating to the extent that the old coating can be seen through the fissures.

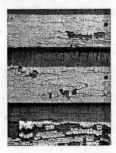

■ **alloy**

substance composed of two or more elements, of which at least one is a metal. These elements are intimately united usually by being dissolved in each other when molten.

■ **alternate deck placement**

a deck pour sequence suggested by the contractor that is contrary to the sequence stated on the plans.

■ **alternating copolymer**

a polymer, composed of two different repeating mers, in which the different mer units systematically alternate positions along the molecular chain.

■ **aluminium roof coating**

fibred or unfibred cutback asphalt coating pigmented with microscopic aluminium flakes.

■ **aluminum**

a lightweight chemical element (Al); the most abundant metallic element in the Earth's crust

■ **ambient**

the natural conditions that would be expected to occur in water un-affected or not influenced by the activities of man.

■ **amine**

materials often used as curing agents for epoxy coatings: any of a class of organic compounds de-rived from ammonia by replace-ment of hydrogen with one or more alkyl groups.

■ **amorphography**

the branch of science concerned with the determination of amor-phous solid structures and their systematic classification (see also **crystallography**).

■ **amorphous**

non-crystalline, without long-range order; lacking organisation or unity

■ **amplifier**

a device, which increases the vol-ume over that of the source flow rate at the expense of pressure, also called a booster. An intensi-fier boosts pressure at cost of flow rate while an amplifier boosts vol-ume at cost of pressure.

■ **amplitude ratio**

the ratio of the control parameter amplitude to the input parameter amplitude at a particular fre-quency.

■ **ampoules**

sealed, liquid-filled tube, which is broken to release or be filled with another fluid.

■ **analogue**

a term pertaining to a general class of devices, components or circuits whose output varies as a continu-ous function of its input over some specific range. For example, a pressure may be represented by a voltage, which is its analogue.

■ **anchor**

piece or assemblage, used to at-tach building parts (e.g., support plates, ties, joists, trusses, etc.) to concrete, masonry or metals. Me-chanical (expansion anchor) or chemical (often a two part resin with or without aggregate) assem-bly used to connect masonry or other veneer to back-up walls.

■ **anchor bolt**

a type of steel bolt used to secure frameworks or wall framing to foundations; also called founda-tion bolt or hold-down.

■ **anchor dowel**

a steel rod used to secure the ends of prestressed concrete units to the substructure.

■ **anchor pattern**

substrate preparation: the surface profile obtained by abrasive treat-ments such as sand blasting or power tool cleaning; may also re-fer to the distance between peaks and valleys of the blast profile.

■ **anchorage**

a secure fixing, usually made of reinforced concrete to which the cables are fastened

■ **anisotropic**

exhibiting different values of a property in different crystallographic directions.

■ **annealed glass**

standard sheet of plate glass..

■ **annealing**

generic term used to denote a controlled heat treatment process, followed by cooling performed on material in the solid state. It is used to remove stresses, to induce softness and to alter the ductility and toughness of metals, glass, or other materials by allowing them to re-crystallise. The temperature of the operation and the rate of cooling will depend upon the metal and the purpose of the annealing.

■ **annulus**

the net area created between two mating rings. For example, the difference between a cylinder bore area and the piston rod area.

■ **anode**

the positive terminal of an electrical source. In a corrosion cell, the anode is the electrode of an electrochemical cell at which oxidation occurs

■ **antenna**

a metallic aerial for sending and receiving electromagnetic waves. A transmitting antenna converts electrical signals from a transmitter into an electromagnetic wave which it then emanates. A receiving antenna intercepts an electromagnetic wave and converts it back into electrical signals that can be decoded by a receiver. Central television, pole and wire, and switching station antennas, as well as satellite dishes, are also included within this category code.

■ **antiferromagnetism**

a phenomenon- observed in some materials in which complete magnetic moment cancellation occurs as a result of antiparallel coupling of adjacent atoms or ions. The macroscopic solid possesses no net magnetic moment.

■ **application rate**

the quantity (mass, volume or thickness) of coating material applied per unit area.

■ **application, water right**

an official request for permission to initiate a water right; includes a description of the proposed project, a map of the project and a legal description of the property involved.

■ **approach**

portion of the highway immediately before or after the bridge.

■ **approach slab**

reinforced concrete slab placed adjacent to abutment to reduce the 'bump' a vehicle may feel due to settlement of the approach fill immediately adjacent to the bridge.

■ **appropriate**

to authorise the use of a quantity of water to an individual requesting it.

■ **appurtenant to place of use**

a water right that belongs to the legal owner of the land described as the place of use on the water right.

■ **apron**

the flat member of the inside trim of a window placed against the wall immediately beneath the stool.

■ **aqua**

prefix meaning water.

■ **aquatic life**

all forms of living things found in water, ranging from bacteria, to fish and rooted plants. Insect larva and zooplankton are also included.

■ **aqueduct**

a bridge or channel for conveying water, usually over long distances.

■ **aquiclude**

a formation, which, although porous and capable of absorbing water slowly, will not transmit water fast enough to furnish an appreciable supply for a well or a spring.

■ **aquifer**

a water bearing stratum of permeable rock, sand, or gravel.

■ **arch bridge**

a curved structure that converts the downward force of its own weight, and of any weight pressing down on top of it, into an outward force along its sides and base

■ **arch dam**

a dam with an arched shape that resists the force of water pressure; requires less material than a gravity dam for the same distance

■ **architect**

a person who designs all kinds of structures; must also have the ability to conceptualise and communicate ideas effectively both in words and on paper to clients, engineers, government officials, and construction crews

■ **area divider**

a raised, flashed assembly (typically a single- or double-wood member attached to a wood base plate) that is anchored to the roof deck. It is used to relieve thermal stresses in a roof system where an expansion joint is not required, or to separate large roof areas (sometimes between expansion joints), and may be used to facilitate installation of tapered insulation.

■ **areaway**

an open subsurface space adjacent to a building used to admit light or air or as a means of access to a basement.

■ **argon**

inert, non-toxic gas used in insulating windows to reduce heat transfer.

■ **arid**

an adjective applied to regions where precipitation is deficient in quantity; where agriculture is impractical without irrigation.

■ **aridity**

the quality or state of being arid, dry or barren.

■ **armoured joint**

one type of bridge joint that accommodates the thermal expansion and contraction of the superstructure. This type of joint uses armouring angles and an elastomeric compression seal.

■ **aromatic hydrocarbons**

a class of relatively strong organic solvents which contain an unsaturated ring of carbon atoms. Examples are benzene, toluene and xylene.

■ **artesian aquifer**

an aquifer where the water is under sufficient head (pressure) to cause it to rise above the zone of saturation if the opportunity were afforded for it to do so.

■ **artesian water**

water that comes from artesian wells.

■ **artesian wall**

1. a well made by drilling into the earth until water is reached, which, from internal pressure, flows up like a fountain.
2. a well tapping a confined or artesian aquifer in, which the static water level stands above the top of the aquifer. The term is sometimes used to include all wells tapping confined water. Wells with water level above the water table are said to have positive artesian head, (pressure) and those with water level below the water table, negative artesian head.

■ **As**

Arsenic.

■ **asbestos**

any of several naturally occurring, fibrous, impure silicate materials; have been implicated as causes of certain cancers, and that have been used in the past as fireproofing and insulating materials.

■ **as-built plans**

set of plans containing all field changes made during construction to the final design plans.

ascrete

open graded asphalt with the addition of cement slurry to provide strong surface resistance to deformation and oil spillage.

ASD

Allowable Stress Design, also known as Working Stress Design

ashlar

masonry composed of (mostly) rectangular units made of cut stone, cultured stone, burned clay or shale, and generally larger in size than regular brick. The ashlar units are properly bonded, having sawed, dressed or squared beds, and joints laid in mortar. Often the unit size varies to provide a random pattern, random ashlar.

asphalt

1. a dark brown to black cementitious material in which the predominating constituents are bitumens, which may occur naturally or are obtained in petroleum refining. It is used as a waterproofing agent, sealant or pavement.
2. a dark brown to black, highly viscous, hydrocarbon products from the residue left after the distillation of petroleum, used as a waterproofing agent.
3. a mixture of bitumen and aggregates (coarse and fine including sand). Produced as hot mix or cold mix. referred to as bc (bituminous concrete) or ac (asphaltic concrete).
4. most native asphalt is a residue from evaporated petroleum. It is insoluble in water. Used widely in building for waterproofing roof coverings of many types, exterior wall coverings, flooring tile, and the like.

asphalt emulsion

a mixture of asphalt particles and an emulsifying agent such as bentonite clay and water. These components are combined by using a chemical or a clay emulsifying agent and mixing or blending machinery.

asphalt felt

a mat of organic or inorganic fibres, impregnated with asphalt or coal tar pitch, or impregnated and coated with asphalt.

asphalt mastic

mixture of asphaltic material and graded mineral aggregate that can be poured when heated, but requires mechanical manipulation to apply when cool.

asphalt, air blown

produced by blowing air through molten asphalt held at an elevated temperature, to raise the asphalt's softening point and modify other properties.

asphaltene

a high molecular weight hydrocarbon fraction precipitated from asphalt by a designated solvent (paraffinic naphtha) at a specified temperature and solvent-asphalt ratio.

asphaltic concrete

refer asphalt.

■ **assessment report**

a comprehensive record of historical, existing and projected water quality conditions of a watershed.

■ **astragal**

a moulding, attached to one of a pair of swinging doors, against which the other door strikes.

■ **atactic**

a type of polymer chain configuration wherein side groups are randomly positioned on one side of the polymer backbone or the other.

■ **atmosphere**

the layer of gases surrounding the earth and composed of considerable hydrogen and oxygen, and when properly combined, water.

■ **atmosphere, standard**

the pressure exerted by the atmosphere at sea level at 15° C and is equal to 14.7 psi, 1.034 kgf/cm² or 1.014 bar.

■ **atmospheric pressure**

the actual pressure exerted on all objects by the atmosphere because of the weight of the surrounding air. Varies with elevation, temperature and climatic conditions.

■ **attached ground water**

the portion of amount of alkali substances sufficient to raise the pH value above 7.0 or to be harmful to the growth of crops. Such a condition is called alkaline.

■ **attenuation**

production of an output signal of smaller magnitude than its corresponding input, sometimes termed a 'gain' of less than 1.0 or an 'amplitude ratio' of less than 1.0.

■ **attic ventilators**

(in houses, screened opening) provided to ventilate an attic space. They are located in the soflit area as inlet ventilators and in the gable end or along the ridge as outlet ventilators. They can also consist of power-driven fans used as an exhaust system.

■ **austenite**

face-centred cubic iron; also iron and steel alloys that have the FCC structure.

■ **automatic**

a sequence of operations, which can take place without operator control.

■ **Average Least Dimension (ALD)**

the average height of the aggregate particles when they are spread as a single layer with their least dimensions vertical

■ **awning**

17th century roof like cover made of fabric, concrete, metal, plastics, etc. which extends over or in front of a place (as over the deck or in front of a door or window) as a shelter

■ **axle load**

the total load on a truck axle. Usually two times the wheel load.

■ **back fill**

1. rough masonry built behind a facing or between two faces

2. brickwork in spaces between structural timbers, sometimes called brick nogging.
3. filling over the extrados of an arch
4. waste material used to fill the void created by excavation or mining.
5. the replacement of excavated earth into a trench around and against a basement foundation.

■ **back nailing**

the practice of nailing roofing felts to the deck under the overlap, in addition to hot mopping, to prevent slippage of felts.

■ **back pressure**

a pressure existing on the discharge or back side of a load. It adds to the pressure required to move the load.

■ **backflow**

the backing up of water through a conduit or channel in the direction opposite to normal flow.

■ **backhand**

a simple moulding sometimes used around the outer edge of plain rectangular casing as a decorative feature.

■ **backing**

the support material consisting of paper, cloth or fibre serving as base for coated abrasives.

■ **backing plate**

in injection moulding, a plate used as a support for the cavity blocks, guide pins, bushing, etc. Also known as support plate.

■ **backlash**

the angular play between meshing gears.

■ **back-nailing**

(also referred to as blind-nailing) the practice of nailing the back portion of a roofing ply, steep roofing unit, or other components in a manner so that the fasteners are covered by the next sequential ply, or course, and are not exposed to the weather in the finished roof system.

■ **backoff**

a rapid withdrawal of cutting tool or grinding wheel from the surface.

■ **back-pressure relief port**

an opening in an extrusion die for escape of excess material.

■ **back-surfacing**

fine mineral matter applied to the back side of asphalt shingles and roll roofing to keep them from sticking together while packaged.

■ **backup**

part of a masonry wall hidden behind the exterior facing. A substitute or support 'a backup plan'; alternate; alternative. Accumulation caused by a stoppage in the flow 'water backup' or 'traffic backup'.

■ **backup ring**

Used to bridge a clearance and minimise extrusion of a seal when cylinder barrel circumferentially expands or when differential pressure across seal is high. It must not collapse or cold flow and sometimes known as an 'anti-extrusion ring.'

■ **backwall**

the portion of the abutment above the level of the bridge seat that primarily acts as a retaining wall. It may also act as a support for the bridge deck and/or the approach slab.

■ **backwash**

water movement against the primary direction of flow

■ **backwater effect**

the effect, which a dam or other obstruction has in raising the surface of the water upstream from it.

■ **backwater flooding**

upstream flooding caused by downstream conditions such as channel restriction and/ or high flow in a downstream confluence stream.

■ **bacterial corrosion**

a corrosion which results from substances (e.g., ammonia or sulphuric acid) produced by the activity of certain bacteria.

■ **baffle**

a partition or grating in a furnace, container or channel

■ **bailer**

device for removing sludge and water from a drill hole or mine

■ **bainite**

a Fe-C composition consisting of a fine dispersion of cementite in alpha-ferrite. It is an austenitic transformation product that forms at temperatures between those at which pearlite and martensite transformations occur.

■ **balance**

a mechanical device (normally spring loaded) used in single- and double-hung windows as a means of counterbalancing the weight of the sash during opening and closing.

■ **balance sheet**

a formal statement of the financial position of a company on a particular day, normally presented to shareholders once a year. Everything owned by the company (i.e. its assets) must be equal to the sum of the company's debts (liabilities) and the value of its shares and retained earnings (net worth)

■ **ballast**

an anchoring material, such as aggregate, or precast concrete pavers, which employ the force of gravity to hold (or assist in holding) single-ply roof membranes in place.

■ **balusters**

usually small vertical members in a railing used between a top rail and the stair treads or a bottom rail.

■ **balustrade**

a railing made up of balusters, top rail, and sometimes bottom rail, used on the edge of stairs, teal conies, and porches.

■ **band gap energy**

for semiconductors and insulators, the energies that lie between the valence and conduction bands.

■ **bank**

the margins of a channel. Banks are called right or left as viewed facing in the direction of the flow.

■ **bankful stage**

an established river stage at a certain point along a river, which is intended to represent the maximum safe water level, which will not overflow the river banks or cause any significant damage within the reach of the river.

■ **bar**

an international measure of pressure equal to 14.5 psi or 1.02 kgf/sqcm.

■ **bare spots**

small areas on a roof where the top membrane has become exposed to the elements.

■ **barge board**

a decorative board covering the projecting rafter (fly rafter) of the gable end. At the cornice, this member is a facie board.

■ **barrel bellowing**

expansion of the cylinder barrel during pressurisation.

■ **barrel roof**

a roof design which in cross section is arched.

■ **barrier coat**

a coating used to isolate a paint system either from the surface to which it is applied or a previous coating for the purpose of increasing adhesion or insuring compatibility

■ **basal till**

unsorted glacial debris at the base of the soil column where it comes into contact with the bedrock below.

■ **basalt**

an extrusive volcanic rock composed primarily of plagioclase, pyroxene and minor olivine.

■ **base**

any compound that will combine with an acid and neutralise it, forming a salt; also bottom or support for any structure

■ **base course**

a layer of asphalt below the wearing course.

■ **base flashing (membrane base flashing)**

plies or strips of roof membrane material used to close-off and/or seal a roof at the roof-to-vertical intersections, such as at a roof-to-wall juncture. Membrane base flashing covers the edge of the field membrane.

■ **base flood**

the national standard for floodplain management is the base, or one percent chance flood. This flood has at least one chance in 100 of occurring in any given year. It is also called a 100 year flood.

■ **base flood elevation**

this is the elevation above the average sea level that waters from a 1% flood will reach at a given point along a creek or bayou. These elevations are determined using hydrology and hydraulic computer models and then these elevations are mapped on the topographic data for the county to produce the 1% floodplain.

■ **base metal**

any non-precious metal (e.g. copper, lead, zinc, nickel, etc.)

■ **base moulding**

moulding used to trim the upper edge of interior baseboard.

■ **base oil**

a base stock fluid without additives.

■ **base or baseboard**

a board placed against the wall around a room next to the floor to finish properly between floor and plaster.

■ **base ply**

an asphalt-saturated and/or coated felt installed as the first ply with 4 inch laps in a built-up roof system under the following felts which can be installed in a shingle like fashion.

■ **base sheet**

an impregnated, saturated, or coated felt placed as the first ply in some multi-ply built-up and modified bitumen roof membranes.

■ **base shoe**

moulding used next to the floor on interior base board. Sometimes called a carpet strip.

■ **baseflow**

streamflow, which results from precipitation that infiltrates into the soil and eventually moves through the soil to the stream channel. This is also referred to as ground water flow, or dry-weather flow.

■ **basic**

underlying fundamental; rocks with little silica; also the opposite of acidic

basic research

fundamental scientific research concerned solely with scientific principles as opposed to applied scientific research which is concerned with the commercial application of those principles

basin boundary

the topographic dividing line around the perimeter of a basin, beyond, which overland flow (i.e.; runoff) drains away into another basin.

batch plant/drum plant

a plant used for the manufacture of asphalt. Can be either a drum mix plant or a batch plant.

batten

narrow strips of wood used to cover joints or as decorative vertical members over plywood or wide boards.

batten plate

a formed piece of metal designed to cover the joint between two lengths of metal edge.

batter

recessing or sloping masonry back in successive courses; the opposite of corbel

batter board

one of a pair of horizontal boards nailed to posts set at the corners of an excavation, used to indicate the desired level, also as a fastening for stretched strings to indicate outlines of foundation walls.

battered pile

a pile that enters the ground at some angle from vertical in order to help resist horizontal forces.

bay window

1. any window space projecting outward from the walls of a building, either square or polygonal in plan.
2. an arrangement of three or more individual window units, attached so as to project from the building at various angles. In a three-unit bay, the centre section is normally fixed, with the end panels operable as single-hung or casement windows.

bead

a wood strip against which a swinging sash closes, as in a casement window. Also, a finishing trim at the sides and top of the frame to hold the sash, as in a fixed sash or a double-hung window. Also referred to as bead stop.

■ **beam**

a heavy main support structure, steel or wood running horizontally between columns or load bearing walls.

■ **beam bridge**

a simple type of bridge, composed of horizontal beams supported by vertical posts

■ **bearing**

a support element used to transfer loads from superstructure to substructure while permitting some rotation and horizontal movement of the superstructure.

■ **bearing partition**

a partition that supports any vertical load in addition to its own weight.

■ **bearing wall**

a wall that supports any vertical load in addition to its own weight.

■ **bed moulding**

a moulding in an angle, as between the over hanging cornice, or eaves, of a building and the side walls.

■ **bedding**

the arrangement of sedimentary rocks in layers.

■ **bedrock**

1. solid rock forming the earth's crust, frequently covered by soil or water.
2. the solid rock layer beneath sand or silt.

■ **beginning of freezeup**

date on, which ice forming a stable winter ice cover is first observed on the water surface.

■ **beginning of the breakup**

date of definite breaking, movement, or melting of ice cover or significant rise of water level.

■ **bench**

a nearly level area placed in front of an abutment or wingwall to provide easy access for future inspection and maintenance.

■ **benchmark**

a survey point with known elevation and coordinates from which other surveys are referenced.

■ **bend**

to curve; bending occurs when a straight material becomes curved; one side squeezes together in compression, and the other side stretches apart in tension.

■ beneficial use of water

the use of water for any beneficial purpose. Such uses include domestic use, irrigation, recreation, fish and wildlife, fire protection, navigation, power, industrial use, etc. The benefit varies from one location to another and by custom. What constitutes beneficial use is often defined by statute or court decisions.

■ bentonite

a clay which has great ability to absorb water and which swells accordingly

■ Bernoulli's law

states that if no work is done on or by a flowing frictionless fluid, its energy due to pressure and velocity remains constant at all points along the streamline. That is, an increase of velocity is always accompanied by a decrease in pressure.

■ best management practice

a practice or combination of practices determined to be the most practicable means of preventing or reducing, to a level compatible with water quality goals, the amount of pollution generated by non-point sources.

■ best practices

concept of achieving a minimum standard for a construction project; to possess the following basic qualities: acceptable aesthetics, solid construction using appropriate materials, and safety

■ beta ratio

an international standard method of expressing the filtration ratio or particle capture characteristics of a hydraulic filter. It is the ratio of the number of particles greater than a given size in the influent fluid to the number of particles greater than the same size in the effluent fluid.

■ bifunctional monomer

a monomer unit that has two active bonding positions.

■ bifurcation

a point where a single lane forks into two lanes.

■ binder

1. the non-volatile portion of the vehicle of a coating which holds together the pigment particles.
2. a material used to bind aggregates. Usually bitumen and bitumen blends.

■ biochemical oxygen demand

the oxygen used in meeting the metabolic needs of aerobic microorganisms in water rich in organic matter.

■ biodegradation

the technology that uses microorganisms to degrade contaminants.

■ biosphere

The part of the world in which life can exist.

■ biota

all the species of plants and animals indigenous to a certain area.

■ bird bath

random, inconsequential amounts of residual water on a roof membrane.

■ bird screen

wire mesh used to prevent birds from entering the building through ventilators, louvers, or other openings. (See **insect screen**.)

■ bitumen

1. a class of amorphous, black or dark coloured, (solid, semi-solid, or viscous) cementitious substances, natural or manufactured, composed principally of high molecular weight hydrocarbons, soluble in carbon disulphide, and found in petroleum asphalts, coal tars and pitches, wood tars and asphalts;

2. a generic term used to denote any material composed principally of bitumen, typically asphalt or coal tar.

■ bituminous coating

a coal tar or asphalt based coating material usually used in thick films.

■ bituminous concrete

refer asphalt.

■ bituminous emulsion

a suspension of minute particles of bituminous material in water or other aqueous solution.

■ blackberry (sometimes referred to as blueberry or tar-boil)

a small bubble or blister in the flood coating of an aggregate-surfaced built-up roof membrane.

■ blackbody

the ideal, perfect emitter and absorber of thermal radiation, it emits radiant energy at each wavelength at the maximum rate possible as a consequence of its temperature, and absorbs all incident radiance.

■ blanket (batt) insulation

fibreglass or other compressible fibrous insulation, generally available in roll form.

■ blast cleaning

the cleaning and roughing of a surface by the use of sand, artificial grit or fine metal shot which is projected at a surface by compressed air or mechanical means.

■ **blast furnace**

a reaction vessel in which mixed charges of oxide ores, fluxes and fuels are blown with a continuous blast of hot air and oxygen-enriched air for the chemical reduction of metals to their metallic state iron ore is most commonly treated in this way, and so are some ores of copper, lead, etc

■ **blast furnace slag**

refer **slag**.

■ **blaster**

a mine employee responsible for loading, priming and detonating blastholes

■ **blasthole, blast hole**

a hole drilled for purposes of blasting rather than for exploration or geological information

■ **blasting**

detonating explosives to loosen rock for excavation

■ **bleaching**

the fading of a colour toward white generally caused by exposure to chemicals or ultraviolet radiation

■ **bleed**

a small controlled flow of fluid from a pressurised system.

■ **bleeding**

the diffusion of colour matter through a coating from underlying surfaces causing colour change

■ **bleed-sheet**

a sheet material used to prevent the migration of bitumen.

■ **blind end**

a cylinder end closure, which completely covers the bore area, called the cap.

■ **blind stop**

a rectangular moulding used in the assembly of a window frame. Serves as a stop for storm and screen or combination windows and to resist air infiltration.

■ **blind-nailing**

nailing in such a way that the nail heads are not visible on the face of the work usually at the tongue of matched boards.

■ **blister**

an enclosed raised spot evident on the surface of a roof. They are mainly caused by the expansion of trapped air, water vapour, moisture or other gases. Blisters on a roof may involve only the coating, one or more plies of felt or may involve the whole membrane thickness.

■ **blister copper**

the product of the bessemer converter furnace used in copper smelting it is a crude form of copper, assaying about 99% copper, and requires further refining before being used for industrial purposes.

■ **block copolymer**

a linear copolymer in which identical mer units are clustered in blocks along the molecular chain.

■ **block diagram**

a diagram representing the flow of information and the functions performed by each component in a system.

■ blocking

sections of wood (which may be preservative treated) built into a roof assembly, usually attached above the deck and below the membrane or flashing, used to stiffen the deck around an opening, act as a stop for insulation, support a curb, or to serve as a nailer for attachment of the membrane and/or flashing.

■ blooming

a haziness which develops on paint surfaces caused by the exudation of a component of the paint film

■ blowdown

the water drawn from boiler systems and cold water basins of cooling towers to prevent the buildup of solids.

■ blowing agent

an expanding agent used to produce a gas by chemical or thermal action, or both, in manufacture of hollow or cellular materials.

■ blue stain

a bluish or greyish discolouration of the sapwood caused the growth of certain mould like fungi on the surface and in the interior of a piece, made possible by the same conditions that favour the growth of other fungi.

■ blushing

a film defect which manifests itself as a milky appearance which is generally caused by rapid solvent evaporation or the presence of excessive moisture during the curing process

■ BMS

Bridge Management System

■ BOCA

Building Officials And Code Administrators

■ bode plot

a chart showing how an output signal differs from its input signal in magnitude and timing as a function of frequency.

■ bodied linseed oil

linseed oil that has been thickened in viscosity by suitable processing with heat or chemicals. Bodied oils are obtainable in a great range in viscosity from a little greater than that of raw oil to just short of a jellied condition.

■ body-centred cubic (BCC)

a common crystal structure that contains atoms located at the corners of a cubic cell and one atom at the cell centre position.

■ boiled linseed oil

linseed oil in which enough lead, manganese or cobalt salts have been incorporated to make the oil harden more rapidly when spread in thin coatings.

■ boiling point

the temperature at, which a liquid boils. It is the temperature at, which the vapour pressure of a liquid equals the pressure on its surface. If the pressure of the liquid varies, the actual boiling point varies. For water it is 212 degrees Fahrenheit or 100 degrees Celsius.

■ **boiling water reactor**

a nuclear reactor in, which water, used as both coolant and moderator, is allowed to boil in the core. The resulting steam can be used directly to drive a turbine generating electric power.

■ **bolster**

a piece of metal, larger than a shim, that takes up the difference in height between two different beams that meet at a pier in lieu of stepping the pedestal.

■ **Boltzmann's constant**

the gas constant per molecule: 1.381×10^{-23} J/atom K; 1.381×10^{-16} erg/atom K; or 8.63×10^{-5} eV/atom K.

■ **BOMA**

Building Owners & Managers Association, International

■ **bond**

1. adhesion between various components and materials, such as adhesion between mortar (or grout) and masonry units or reinforcement.
2. patterns formed by exposed faces of units
3. tying various parts of a masonry wall by lapping units one over another or by connecting with metal ties

4. attachment between a (coating) film and the substrate material to which it is applied
5. a form of insurance agreement under which a bonding company guarantees to pay an owner or developer within stated limits for any financial loss, or for failure of the binder (contractor) to perform in accordance with the terms of the contract, i.e., to follow specifications, to charge the agreed-upon price, or to otherwise be found in default of the contract
6. process of joining two structures together, i.e., to create an assembly by means of adhesive linkage

■ **bond beam**

course or courses of a masonry wall grouted and usually reinforced in the horizontal direction serves as horizontal tie of wall, bearing course for structural members or as a flexural member itself.

■ **bond breaker**

a substance or a tape applied between two adjoining materials to prevent adhesion between them.

■ **bond course**

the course consisting of units which overlap more than one wythe of masonry.

■ **bond, chemical**

adhesion between surfaces, usually of similar materials, resulting from a chemical reaction or cross-linking of polymer chains.

■ **bond, mechanical**

adhesion between surfaces resulting from interfacial forces or a physical interlocking.

■ **bonding agent**

a chemical substance applied to a suitable substrate to create bond between it and a succeeding layer.

■ **bonding energy**

the energy required to separate two atoms that are chemically bonded to each other.

■ **boom**

telescoping, (usually) hydraulically powered steel arm used to deliver hoses (such as in concrete pumping), man baskets or hydraulic hammers to the work location on a particular site.

■ **booster**

a device, which increases the volume over that of the system flow rate at the expense of pressure, also called an amplifier. It is the adverse of an intensifier, which amplifies pressure at the expense of flow rate.

■ **boot**

1. a covering made of flexible material, which may be preformed to a particular shape, used to exclude dust, dirt, moisture, etc. from around a penetration;

2. a flexible material used to form a closure, sometimes installed at inside and outside corners.

■ **borehole**

common term for a drill hole

■ **borer**

common term for rock-cutting drill

■ **boring**

a soil exploration technique of drilling into the ground at various locations in an attempt to construct an accurate subsurface profile.

■ **borrow pit**

an excavated area where soil, sand, or gravel has been dug up for use elsewhere.

■ **Boston ridge**

a method of applying asphalt or wood shingles at the ridge or at the hips of a roof as a finish.

■ **bottom rail**

the bottom horizontal member of a window sash

■ **bounce back**

the rebound of atomised paint, especially when applied by conventional air spray methods

■ **bound material**

a mixture of fine and coarse aggregates bound together with bitumen, cement etc..

■ **boundary lubrication**

a lubrication regime in, which mating surfaces are in rubbing contact and where the lubricating film between the surfaces has a thickness approximately equal to the surface roughness of the contacting surfaces.

■ **bow window**

rounded bay window that projects from the wall in an arc shape.

■ **boxing**

mixing of coatings by pouring from one container to another.

■ **brace**

an inclined piece of framing lumber applied to wall or floor to stifled the structure. Often used on walls as temporary bracing until framing has been completed.

■ **Bragg's law**

a relationship that stipulates the condition for diffraction by a set of crystallographic planes.

■ **braid neutral angle**

the angle 54°44' is called the neutral angle of hose braid because it is the angle at which there is no movement of the hose, under internal pressure, either in hose length or diameter, assuming no elongation of the reinforcement. At the neutral angle, the braid offers maximum resistance to both hoop and longitudinal stresses and will therefore be in a state of equi-

librium when the hose is subject to internal pressure.

■ **brake metal**

sheet metal that has been bent to the desired configuration.

■ **branched polymer**

a polymer having a molecular structure of secondary chains that extend from the primary chains.

■ **brasing**

method of joining metal pieces by using a nonferrous filler metal heated below the melting point of the base metals to be joined, but above 800° F (430° C). The filler metal, also called hard solder, may be brass, bronze, or a silver or gold alloy; the filler metal distributes itself between the surfaces to be bonded by capillarity. Brasing is different from welding; in welding, partial melting of the surfaces is likely to occur, and the filler metal is not distributed by capillarity. Brasing differs from soldering only in the temperature of the operation. Ordinary, or soft, solder melts at temperatures below 430° C. To reduce any oxide film on the surfaces in manufacturing operations, furnaces are often used to heat the parts to be brased, or the parts are brased by dipping in baths of molten filler alloys for construction site operations, the joint is usually preheated with a gas torch

■ **brass**

a copper-rich copper-zinc alloy.

■ **brazing**

a metal joining technique that uses a molten filler metal alloy having a melting temperature greater than about 425°C.

■ **breaking joints**

any arrangement of masonry units which prevents continuous vertical joints from occurring in adjacent courses

■ **breakup**

the time when a river whose surface has been frozen from bank to bank for a significant portion of its length begins to change to an open water flow condition. Breakup is signalled by the breaking of the ice and often associated with ice jams and flooding.

■ **breakup date**

date on, which a body of water is first observed to be entirely clear of ice and remains clear thereafter.

■ **breakup jam**

ice jam that occurs as a result of the accumulation of broken ice pieces.

■ **breakup period**

the period of disintegration of an ice cover.

■ **breather**

a device, which allows air to move in and out of a container to compensate for fluctuating levels of liquid to maintain atmospheric pressure.

■ **brick**

a solid masonry unit of clay or shale, formed into a rectangular prism while plastic and burned or fired in a kiln. It is of the following types:

1. acid-resistant brick suitable for use in contact with chemicals, usually in conjunction with acid-resistant mortars.

2. adobe brick large roughly-moulded, sun-dried clay brick of varying size.

3. angle brick any brick shaped to an oblique angle to fit a salient corner.

4. arch brick a wedge-shaped brick for special use in an arch; extremely hard-burned brick from an arch of a scove kiln.

5. building brick for building purposes not especially treated for texture or colour, formerly called common brick.

6. clinker brick, a very hard-burned brick whose shape is distorted or bloated due to nearly complete vitrification.

7. common brick see **building brick.**

8. dry-press brick formed in moulds under high pressures from relatively dry clay (5 to 7 percent moisture content).

9. economy brick whose nominal dimensions are 4 by 4 by 8 in.

10. engineered brick whose nominal dimensions are 4 by 32 by 8 in.

11. facing brick made especially for facing purposes, often treated to produce surface texture. They are made of selected clays, or treated to produce desired colour.

12. fire brick made of refractory ceramic material which will resist high temperatures

13. floor brick: smooth dense brick, highly resistant to abrasion, used as finished floor surfaces.

14. gauged brick: a brick which have been ground or otherwise produced to accurate dimensions by a tapered arch brick.

15. hollow brick: a masonry unit of clay or shale whose net cross-sectional area in any plane parallel to the bearing surface is not less than 60 percent of its gross cross-sectional area measured in the same plane.

16. jumbo brick: a generic term, indicating a brick larger in size than the standard. Some producers use this term to describe oversize brick of specific dimensions manufactured by them.

■ brick and brick

a method of laying brick so that units touch each other with only enough mortar to fill surface irregularities

■ brick grade

designation for durability of the unit expressed as SW for severe weathering, mw for moderate weathering, or NW for negligible weathering.

■ brick moulding

wood trim piece that covers the gap between the window frame and masonry

■ brick type

designation for facing brick which controls tolerance, chippage and distortion expressed as FBS, FBX and FBA for solid brick, and HBS, HBX, HBA and HBB for hollow brick.

■ brick veneer

a facing of brick laid against and fastened to sheathing of a frame wall or tile wall construction.

■ bridge seat

horizontal surface of the abutment stem upon which rest the pedestals and/or the bearings.

■ bridging

the formation of a paint film over a depression. Small wood or metal members that are inserted in a diagonal position between the floor joists at mid-span to act both as tension and compression members for the purpose of bracing the joists a spreading the action of loads.

■ brine

water that is saturated or partially saturated with salt.

■ British thermal unit (BTU)

the heat energy required to raise the temperature of one pound of water one degree Fahrenheit (joule).

■ brittle

characteristic of a material that fails without warning; brittle materials do not stretch or shorten before failing.

■ **brittle fracture**

fracture that occur by rapid crack propagation and without appreciable macroscopic deformation.

■ **brittleness**

the lack of resistance to cracking or breaking of a paint film when bent or flexed.

■ **bronze**

a copper-rich copper-tin alloy.

■ **brooming**

an action carried out to facilitate embedment of a ply of roofing material into hot bitumen by using a broom, squeegee, or special implement to smooth out the ply and ensure contact with the bitumen or adhesive under the ply.

■ **brownfields**

abandoned, idled, or under-used industrial and commercial facilities where expansion or redevelopment is complicated by real or perceived environmental contamination

■ **brush curb**

a curb used with steel railings to channel water off of a bridge and preventing it from falling onto the feature crossed.

■ **brushability**

the ease of applying a coating by brush

■ **BTU**

abbreviation for British Thermal Unit the amount of heat required to increase the temperature of one pound of water one degree Fahrenheit

■ **bubbling**

a temporary or permanent film defect in which bubbles of air or solvent vapour are present in the applied film

■ **buck**

often used in reference to rough frame opening members. Door bucks used in reference to metal door frame.

■ **buckle**

an upward, elongated tenting displacement of a roof membrane frequently occurring over insulation or deck joints. A buckle may be an indication of movement within the roof assembly.

■ **buffer strip/zone**

strips of grass or other erosion resistant vegetation between a waterway and an area of more intensive land use.

■ **building code**

published regulations and ordinances established by a recognised agency prescribing design loads, procedures, and construction details for structures. Usually applying to designated jurisdictions (city, county, state, etc.). Building codes control design, construction, and quality of materials, use and occupancy, location and maintenance of buildings and structures within the area for which the code has been adopted.

■ **built environment**

all human-built-structures. In the green builder program, the built environment pertains to single-family-homes only.

■ built-up roof

a roofing composed of three to five layers of asphalt felt laminated with coal tar, pitch, or asphalt. The top is finished with crushed slag or gravel. Generally used on flat or low-pitched roofs.

■ built-up roof

a roof consisting minimally of a bur membrane but may also include insulation, vapour retarders and other components.

■ built-up roof membrane

a continuous, semi-flexible multiply roof membrane, consisting of plies or layers of saturated felts, coated felts, fabrics, or mats between which alternate layers of bitumen are applied. Generally, built-up roof membranes are surfaced with mineral aggregate and bitumen, a liquid-applied coating, or a granule-surfaced cap sheet.

■ built-up roof membrane

a built-up roof consisting of plies or layers of roofing felt bonded together on site with bitumen; either tar or asphalt.

■ bulb-tee

a specialised steel reinforcing member which support form boards and reinforces a gypsum deck, which when poured surrounds the bulb-tee.

■ bulk density

can refer to the density of the aggregate or the density of compacted asphalt. Typically asphalt is 2.3 to 2.5 t/m³.

■ bulk modulus

a measure of resistance to compressibility of a fluid and is the reciprocal of compressibility.

■ bulk modulus, effective

the bulk modulus of the system, which includes the elasticity of the container, the amount of gas present in the liquid, and the compressibility of the liquid itself.

■ buoyancy

the tendency of a body to float or rise when immersed in a fluid; the power of a fluid to exert an upward force on a body placed in it.

■ burgers vector

a vector that denotes the magnitude and direction of lattice distortion associated with a dislocation.

■ butt joint

the junction where the ends of two timbers or other members meet in a square-cut joint.

■ butterfly roof

a roof assembly which pitches sharply from either side toward the centre.

■ buttress

a support that transmits a force from a roof or wall to another supporting structure

■ buttress dam

a gravity dam reinforced by structural supports.

■ butyl

rubber-like material produced by copolymerising isobutylene with a small amount of isoprene. Butyl may be manufactured in sheets, or blended with other elastomeric materials to make sealants and adhesives.

■ butyl coating

an elastomeric coating system derived from polymerised isobutylene. Butyl coatings are characterised by low water vapour permeability.

■ butyl rubber

a synthetic elastomer based on isobutylene and a minor amount of isoprene. It is vulcanisable and features low permeability to gases and water vapour.

■ butyl tape

a sealant tape sometimes used between metal roof panel seams and end laps; also used to seal other types of sheet metal joints, and in various sealant applications.

■ by-pass

a secondary passage for fluid flow, which changes the operation of a component or circuit.

■ C

Carbon.

■ C.I.P.

Cast-In-Place

■ c/b ratio

the ratio of the weight of water absorbed by a masonry unit during immersion in cold water to weight absorbed during immersion in boiling water. An indication of the probable resistance of brick to freezing and thawing. Also called saturation coefficient.

■ cable

a structural element formed from steel wire bound in strands; the suspending element in a bridge; the supporting element in some dome roofs

■ cable-stayed bridge

a bridge in which the roadway deck is suspended from cables anchored to one or more towers

■ cadmium stearate

a heat and light stabiliser, used when good clarity is desired.

■ **cady test**

used for the determination of bursting strength with specific equipment.

■ **caisson**

large diameter cast-in-place deep foundation units.

■ **caisson**

a watertight, dry chamber in which people can work underwater.

■ **calcination**

a high-temperature reaction whereby one solid material dissociates to form a gas and another solid.

■ **calender**

a machine with two or more counter-rotating steel rollers used for laminating sheeting or skim coating (topping) to a controlled thickness or surface characteristic, or both.

■ **calendering**

a manufacturing process by which some polymeric membranes and other sheetings are produced.

■ **calibrate**

the hydrology and hydraulic computer models used to determine the floodplains are checked using actual data from real events.

■ **calibration**

fine tuning of an instrument to meet a specific standard value. This helps to ensure data accuracy.

■ **caliche**

calcium carbonate in earth, common to semi-arid parts. It makes an especially hard brick without firing and is a common roadbed material. It is not commercially available at this time as a brick.

■ **calorie**

this word has more than one definition. A calorie is a unit of heat energy equal to the amount of heat needed to raise the temperature of one gram water one degree Celsius. The calorie is used when temperature is measured on the Celsius scale. The British Thermal Unit is used when the measurement is on the Fahrenheit scale. One calorie equals 4.14 joules. A calorie is also the amount of food, which contains the energy producing value of one calorie.

■ **camber**

vertical curvature built-in to a beam during its fabrication to account for the dead load deflections of the structure. Camber above level is referred to as 'positive camber'.

■ **canopy**

any overhanging or projecting roof structure, typically over entrances or doors. Sometimes the extreme end is unsupported.

■ **cant**

a bevelling of foam at a right angle joint for strength and water run off.

■ **cant strip**

1. a bevelled support used at the intersection of the roof deck with vertical surfaces so that bends in the roofing membrane to form

base flashings can be made without breaking the felts.

2. a triangular shaped piece of lumber used at the junction of a flat deck and a wall to prevent cracking of the roofing which is applied over it.

■ **cantilever**

a projecting structure supported only at one end, like a shelf bracket or a diving board.

■ **cap**

a layer of material, such as clay or a synthetic material, used to prevent rainwater from penetrating and spreading contaminated materials. The surface of the cap is generally mounded or sloped so water will drain off.

■ **cap flashing**

usually composed of metal, used to cover or shield the upper edges of the membrane base flashing, wall flashing, or primary flashing.

■ **cap sheets**

one to four plies of felt bonded and top coated with bitumen that is laid over an existing roof as a treatment for defective roofs.

■ **cap, cylinder**

a cylinder end closure, which completely covers the bore area (opposite the rod end).

■ **capability**

a measure of operational or system effectiveness.

■ **capacitance**

the charge-storage ability of a capacitor, defined as the magnitude of charge stored on either plate divided by the applied voltage.

■ **capacitance meter**

a device used to locate moisture or wet materials within a roof system by measuring the ratio of the change to the potential difference between two conducting elements separated by a non-conductor.

■ **capbeam**

the capbeam transfers concentrated loads from the superstructure to the pier columns or stem. It may also serve to hold pier columns in proper position relative to each other.

■ **capillarity**

the property of tubes or earthlike particles with hairlike openings, which, when immersed in a fluid, raise (or depress) the fluid in the tubes above (or below) the surface. Of the fluid in, which they are immersed.

■ **capillary**

a tube, which exhibits a (length to diameter ratio) 400. In most cases the tube has an internal diameter in the range of a few thousandths of an inch,, which causes the characteristic elevation or depression of liquids.

■ **capillary action**

the action that causes movement of liquids by surface tension when in contact with two adjacent surfaces such as panel side laps.

■ **capillary fringe**

an area in the ground into which capillary water has moved.

■ **capillary phenomena**

a phenomenon- of water movement caused by capillarity.

■ **capillary water**

a continuous film of water found around soil particles.

■ **capillary zone**

the area extending from the water table to the limit of the capillary rise of the water.

■ **carbon absorption**

a treatment system in which contaminants are removed from ground water and surface water by forcing water through tanks containing activated carbon, a specially treated material that attracts and holds or retains contaminants.

■ **carbon dioxide (CO_2)**

a colourless, odourless, incombustible gas that is considered to be a major contributor to global warming. It is a by-product of all combustion processes.

■ **carbon monoxide (CO)**

a colourless, odourless gas resulting from incomplete combustion. Gas stoves, fireplaces, kerosene appliances, tobacco smoke, and automobile exhaust are potential sources. Proper ventilation is important to prevent negative health effects such as fatigue, dizziness and nausea.

■ **carburising**

the process by which the surface carbon concentration of a ferrous alloy is increased by diffusion from the surrounding environment.

■ **carriageway**

the portion of road used by vehicles. Includes the shoulders and auxiliary lanes.

■ **cartridge**

a component, which can be removed and replaced easily without being fully dismantled e.g., a replaceable element for a filter, pump or valve.

■ **cartridge valve**

a valve, which can be removed and replaced easily without being fully dismantled. They are completely bodiless and capable of satisfying directional, flow, and pressure functions.

■ **casement**

a window sash that swings open on side hinges; in-swinging are French in origin; out-swinging are from England.

■ **casement frames and sash**

frames of wood or metal enclosing part or all of the sash, which may be opened by means of hinges affixed to the vertical edges.

■ **casing**

1. exposed moulding or framing around a window or door, on ei-

ther the inside or outside, to cover the space between the window frame or jamb and the wall.
2. moulding of various widths and thickness used to trim door and window openings at the jambs.

■ **cast iron**

a brittle alloy with high carbon content iron that has been melted, then poured into a form and cooled can be made into any shape desired.

■ **cast-in-place**

concrete that is poured and cured in its final position at the project site.

■ **catalyst**

an accelerator, activator or curing agent which chemically increases the rate of reaction in a coating.

■ **cathode**

the negative terminal of an electrolytic cell, which in the corrosion process is protected and not attacked.

■ **cathodic**

with regard to metal and galvanic response, cathodic metals are lower in the galvanic series. (May be protected by the more anodic metals.)

■ **cathodic protection**

a means of corrosion prevention whereby electrons are supplied to the structure to be protected from an external source such as another more reactive metal or a dc power supply.

■ **cathodic protection**

the reduction or prevention of corrosion of a metal surface

caused by making it cathodic. This is accomplished by using a sacrificial anode (such as in zinc rich coatings or galvanising) or by using impressed current.

■ **caulk**

a material (usually a composition of vehicle and pigment) used for filling/sealing joints or junctures, where no elastomeric properties are required.

■ **caulking**

a mastic compound for filling joints and sealing cracks to prevent leakage of water and air, commonly made of silicone, bituminous, acrylic, or rubber-based material

■ **caustic**

a strong base or alkaline material.

■ **caustic soda**

a common name for sodium hydroxide, a strong base or alkali.

■ **cavern**

a large underground opening in rock (usually limestone), which occurred when some of the rock was dissolved by water. In some igneous rocks, caverns can be formed by large gas bubbles.

■ **cavitation**

a localised vaporous/gaseous condition within a liquid stream, which occurs where the pressure is reduced below atmospheric and the vapour pressure of the liquid. In pumps it occurs when the suction line is restricted and the resulting vacuum causes the fluid to boil and the surface of the fluid wetted component to flake and pit.

■ cavity

the cavity or air space between the brick and the positive water barrier at the exterior steel stud wall should not be less than two inches wide. Smaller cavities are permitted but often do not function well. The cavity acts to provide a buffer for wind driven rain and allows water that penetrates the brick veneer to flashing, the cavity should be kept clear of any obstructions that might allow water to bridge across. Mortar droppings should be prevented from falling into the cavity. When mortar droppings do enter the cavity they should be removed. Cavity spaces can be wider, but this will reduce the capacity of the brick ties. Construction tolerance on the cavity width should be limited to ± 1/2".

■ cavity wall

a wall built or arranged to provide an air space within the wall (with or without insulating material), in which the inner and outer materials are tied together by structural framing.

■ cell

this word has more than one definition. It can be a container of chemicals used to make electricity flow in a circuit; and it is also the basic building block of all living matter. The cell of a living thing contains a high percentage of water. In solid waste disposal, one of a series of holes in a landfill where waste is dumped, compacted, and covered with layers of dirt.

■ cellosolve

proprietary name for ethylene glycol monoethyl ether. A slow evaporating, water miscible, relatively strong solvent often used in epoxy coatings.

■ cellulose

the fibrous part of plants used in making paper and textiles,, which in turn may be made into building products.

■ cellulose insulation with borates

cellulose insulation made from recycled newspaper treated with borates to provide fire and vermin protection. Most cellulose insulation available now uses chemical fire retardants as opposed to natural borates. (Environmentally-sensitive persons are commonly warned to avoid cellulose insulation. The ink in the newspaper may cause allergic reactions.)

■ cement

powder of alumina, silica, lime, iron oxide, and magnesium oxide burned together in a kiln and finely ground; used as an ingredient of mortar, grout and concrete; also: ather mixtures used for similar purposes. Concrete; this is an improper usage! something serving to unite firmly. Plastic composition made especially of zinc or silica for filling dental cavities. The fine-grained groundmass or glass of a porphyry. To unite or make firm by or as if by cement. To overlay with concrete; to become cemented

■ **cement mortar**

mortar containing up to four parts of sand, one of cement, and adequate water

■ **cement plug**

hardened cement material filling a portion of a borehole.

■ **cementite**

iron carbide (Fe_3C).

■ **cementitious**

having the properties of cement. Cement is the primary binding agent in concrete.

■ **cementitious coatings**

a coating containing portland cement as one of its components held on the surface by a binder.

■ **cementitious foam insulation**

a magnesium oxide-based material blown with air to create an inert, effective insulation. It may be especially helpful for people with chemical sensitivities. It is not readily available in Texas at this time. It requires certified installers.

■ **cementitious material**

having the property of or acting like cement (i.e. Binding substances together when reacting with water), such as certain lime stones and tuffs when used in the surfacing of roads, but also portland cement and fly ash in concrete, mortar or grout mixes

■ **cement-modified soil**

the addition relatively small amounts of cement (1% to 2%) to fine-grained soils to reduce the liquid limit, plasticity index, volume change and water-retaining tendency. The effect of the cement is to bring individual soil particles into aggregations, thus artificially adjusting the grading of the soil, and increasing its load bearing capacity and shearing strength. This is different from cement which contains more cement also called 'soil stabilisation'.

■ **centipoise**

one hundredth of a poise which is a unit of measurement for viscosity. Water at room temperature has a viscosity of 1.0 centipoise.

■ **centistoke**

a unit of kinematic viscosity. cSt

■ **centring**

temporary formwork for the support of masonry arches or lintels during construction. Also called centre(s)

■ **ceramic**

inorganic, non-metallic products for which the interatomic bonding is predominantly ionic.

■ **ceramic colour glaze**

an opaque coloured glaze of satin or gloss finish obtained by spraying the clay body with a compound of metallic oxides, chemicals and clays. It is burned at high temperatures, fusing glaze to body making them inseparable.

■ **cermet**

a composite material consisting of a combination of ceramic and metallic materials.

■ **certified sustainably managed**

some certifying organisations have been established that oversee the harvesting of wood for lumber. The underlying guideline is preservation of a diverse forest that exhibits the same ecological characteristics as a healthy natural forest. There are few wood products presently being certified.

■ **CFC/HCFC**

Chlorofluorocarbon (CFC) and hydrogen chlorofluorocarbon (HCFC) are considered major contributors to the destruction of the Earth's ozone layer. HCFC is 1/20th as potent as CFC in its ozone-destroying capacity. Any amount of additional threat to the ozone layer can be dangerous, due to the long term potency of CFCs. The current ozone damage is generally attributed to CFCs released 10 to 15 years ago. Twenty percent of ozone damage is caused by CRCs in insulation.

■ **CFM**

Cubic Feet Per Minute.

■ **CFS (cubic feet per second)**

the flow rate or discharge equal to one cubic foot (of water, usually) per second. This rate is equivalent to approximately 7.48 gallons per second. This is also referred to as a second-foot.

■ **CFS-day**

the volume of water discharged in twenty four hours, with a flow of one cubic foot per second is widely used; 1 cfs-day is 24 x 60 x 60 = 86,000 cubic feet, 1.983471 acre-feet, or 646,317 gallons. The average flow in cubic feet per second for any time period is the volume of flow in cfs-days.

■ **chalk**

the resulting dust which occurs on a surface that is susceptible to ultra violet degradation.

■ **chalking**

the formation of a friable powdery coating on the surface of a paint film, generally caused by exposure to ultraviolet radiation resulting in a loss of gloss.

■ **chamfer**

a beveled corner.

■ **channel (watercourse)**

an open conduit either naturally or artificially created, which periodically, or continuously contains moving water, or forms a connecting link between two bodies of water. River, creek, run, branch, anabranch, and tributary are some of the terms used to describe natural channels. Natural channels may be single or braided. Canal and floodway are some of the terms used to describe artificial channels.

■ **channel inflow**

water,, which at any instant, is flowing into the channel system form surface flow, subsurface flow, base flow, and rainfall that has directly fallen onto the channel.

■ **channel lead**

an elongated opening in the ice cover caused by a water current.

■ **channel routing**

The process of determining progressively timing and shape of the flood wave at successive points along a river.

■ **channelisation**

the modification of a natural river channel; may include deepening, widening, or straightening.

■ **charge pressure**

the pressure at, which replenishing fluid is forced into the hydraulic system (above atmospheric pressure).

■ **chase**

a continuous recess built into a wall to receive pipes, ducts, etc.

■ **chatter**

Instability of a hydraulic component. Usually associated with servovalve/actuator combinations, check valves, and relief valves. This instability manifests itself as a clattering sound or in the case of spring biased valves as a loud howl.

■ **check dam**

a small dam constructed in a gully or other small water course to decrease the streamflow velocity, minimise channel erosion, promote deposition of sediment and to divert water from a channel.

■ **check rail**

the bottom horizontal member of the upper sash and the top horizontal member of the lower sash which meet at the middle of a double-hung window.

■ **check valve**

a valve, which normally allows flow in one direction only.

■ **checking**

cracks in the surface of a paint film. A pattern of surface cracks running in irregular lines. When found in the top pour of an asphalt built-up roof, is the preliminary stage of alligatoring. Fissures that appear with age in many exterior paint coatings, at first superficial, but which in time may penetrate entirely through the coating.

■ **checkrails**

meeting rails sufficiently thicker than a window to fill the opening between the top and bottom sash made by the parting stop in the frame of double-hung windows. They are usually bevelled.

■ **chemical formula**

chemical symbols written together to show the atoms in a molecule, such as H_2O (water).

■ **chemical set cement**

a cement that sets through reaction or precipitation. Often subjected to a high temperature during manufacture or use.

■ **chemical stability**

the resistance possessed by a fluid to chemical decomposition; e.g., oxidation, and hydrolysis.

■ **chipping**

small pieces of paint removed from the surface, typically a sign of physical damage incurred in shipping or handling. Use of a surface tolerant primer for touch up followed by the same finish coat generally solves the problem.

■ **chlorinated hydrocarbons**

these include a class of persistent, broad-spectrum insecticides that linger in the environment and accumulate in the food chain. Among them are DDT, aldrin, dieldrin, heptachlor, chlordane, lindane, endrine, mirex, hexachloride, and toxaphene. Other examples include TCE, used as industrial solvent.

■ **chlorinated polyethylene (cpe)**

a thermoplastic material, used for single-ply roof membranes, composed of high molecular weight polyethylene which has been chlorinated, a process that yields a flexible rubber-like material.

■ **chlorinated rubber**

a coating resin formed by the reaction of rubber with chlorine gas. Often used for chemical or water resistant properties.

■ **chlorophyll A**

a green photosynthetic colouring matter of plants found in chloroplasts and made up chiefly of a blue black ester.

■ **chlorosulphonated polyethylene (CSPE or CSM)**

a synthetic, rubber-like thermoset material, based on high molecular weight polyethylene with suphonyl chloride, usually formulated to produce a self-vulcanising membrane. Classified by ASTM Standard D 5019-89.

■ **choke**

a restriction, which is relatively long with respect to its cross-section dimension.

■ **chord**

the shortest distance between two points on a curve.

■ **chute spillway**

the overall structure, which allows water to drop rapidly through an open channel without causing erosion. Usually constructed near the edge of dams.

■ **circuit**

an arrangement of components and interconnecting lines, which form the complete path of flow in a hydraulic system.

■ **circuit relief**

see **system protector**.

■ **circuit, logic control**

a circuit that gathers and processes LOGIC information used to control an output.

■ **circulate**

to move in a circle, circuit or orbit' to flow without obstruction to follow a course that returns to the starting point. Water can circulate in a variety of ways.

■ **citizen monitoring**

a program conducted by students or other volunteers involving the collection, management and dissemination of environmental information.

■ **civil engineer**

an engineer who plans, designs, and supervises the construction of facilities essential to modern life.

■ **civil engineering**

the branch of engineering concerned with the planning, design, engineering and construction of a variety of structures, buildings and facilities for public, commercial and industrial uses.

■ **Cl**

chlorine.

■ **cladding**

a material used as the exterior wall enclosure of a building.

■ **clay**

a natural, mineral aggregate consisting essentially of hydrous aluminium silicate; it is plastic when sufficiently wetted, rigid when dried and vitrified when fired to a sufficiently high temperature.

■ **clay mortar-mix**

finely ground clay used as a plasticiser for masonry mortars.

■ **clean and dry**

rather than a method, the requirement for clean and dry describes the condition of the surface prior to painting. The surface shall be clean, dry, and free of oil, grease, wax, form oils, and any other contaminant that may effect the adhesion of the coating. For best results and high performance requirements remove latencies and contaminants from pre-cast and cast-in-place concrete by abrasive blasting or high pressure water blasting. Dry means that the substrate contains less then 15% moisture.

■ **cleaner**

a detergent, alkali, acid or similar contamination removing material, which is usually water borne.

■ **cleanliness code**

the ISO/SAE Solid Contaminant Code is the only international standard for defining the contamination level of a hydraulic fluid.

■ **clear ceramic glaze**

same as ceramic colour glaze except that it is translucent or slightly tinted, with a gloss finish.

■ **clearance**

the clear distance between two surfaces.

■ **clearance flow**

fluid flow through the space between two mating parts. Such space is needed to achieve easy relative motion and to compensate for differing thermal expansions.

■ **cleat**

a device made of formed sheet metal which is mechanically attached onto which the fascia flange of a metal edge is snapped, so as to protect against wind uplift.

■ **clerestory**

a window in the upper part of a lofty room that admits light to the centre of the room.

■ **climate**

the long-time weather conditions of a particular place. The overall kind of weather of an environment over a period of years; the average course or condition of the weather in a particular place over a period of years, as exhibited by temperature, wind velocity, and precipitation.

■ **climatic cycle**

the periodic changes climate, including a series of dry years following a series of years with heavy rainfall.

■ **clip**

a portion of a brick cut to length.

■ **closed basin**

a basin draining to some depression or pond within its area, from, which water is lost only by evaporation or percolation. A basin without a surface outlet for precipitation falling precipitation.

■ **closed basin lake flooding**

flooding that occurs on lakes with either no outlet or a relatively small one. Seasonal increases in rainfall cause the lake level to rise faster than it can drain. The water may stay at flood stage for weeks, months, or years.

■ **closed centre**

a description given to a directional valve in, which all ports are blocked when it is in the neutral or null position.

■ **closed circuit**

a conduit arrangement in, which the pump delivery, after passing through the hydraulic actuator, bypasses the reservoir and returns directly to the pump inlet. Closed circuit configuration is commonly used in hydrostatic transmission drive systems. The movement of the actuator in this type circuit is controlled by a variable displacement pump and not a valve.

■ **closed loop**

a group of control elements linked together such that the output is continually monitored and compared with the input. Should the output differ from the input, the resulting error signal will cause corrective action in the system.

■ **closer**

the last masonry unit laid in a course. It may be whole or a portion of a unit.

■ **closure**

the process by, which a landfill stops accepting wastes and is shut-down under.

■ **closure strip**

a metal or resilient strip, such as neoprene foam, used to close openings created by joining metal panels or sheets and flashings.

■ **cloudburst**

a torrential downpour of rain,, which by it spottiness and relatively high intensity suggests the bursting and discharge of water from a cloud all at once.

■ **coal slurry pipeline**

a pipeline, which transports pulverized coal suspended in liquid, usually water.

■ **coal tar**

a dark brown to black coloured, semi-solid hydrocarbon obtained as residue from the partial evaporation or distillation of coal tars. Coal tar pitch is further refined to conform to the following roofing grade specifications:

■ **coal tar epoxy**

a coating in which the binder or vehicle is a combination of coal tar and epoxy resins.

■ **coal tar felt**

a felt that has been saturated with refined coal tar.

■ **coal tar pitch (tar)**

a bituminous material which is a by product from the coking of coal. It is used as the waterproofing material for tar and gravel built-up roofing.

■ **coal tar roof cement**

a trowelable mixture of processed coal tar base, solvents, mineral fillers and/or fibres.

■ **coal tar waterproofing pitch**

a coal tar used as the dampproofing or waterproofing agent in below-grade structures.

■ **coalescence**

the formation of resinous or polymeric material when water evaporates from an emulsion or a latex system, permitting contact and fusion of adjacent particles; fusing or flowing together of liquid particles.

■ **coarse aggregate**

a general term for aggregate of such size that it is substantially retained on a sieve of specified size, commonly 4.75 mm.

■ **coarse orange peel surface texture**

a surface showing a texture where nodules and valleys are approximately the same size and shape. This surface is acceptable for receiving a protective coating because of the roundness of the nodules and valleys. The theoretical covering rate cannot be used without adding a mini-mum of 25% additional material.

■ **coat**

the layer of paint (or even plaster) applied to a surface in a single application to form a film when dry.

■ **coated base sheet**

a felt that has previously been saturated (filled or impregnated) with asphalt and later coated with harder, more viscous asphalt, which greatly increases its impermeability to moisture.

■ **coated fabric**

fabrics that have been impregnated and/or coated with a plastic-like material in the form of a solution, dispersion hot-melt, or powder. The term also applies to materials resulting from the application of a preformed film to a fabric by means of calendering.

■ **coating**

1. material applied to a surface in order to protect, preserve, seal, decorate, or smooth the substrate. 2. a layer of any brush consistency product spread over a surface for protection.

■ **coating asphalt**

weather-resistant layer of asphalt applied to a roofing material surface during manufacture. surfacing material such as aggregate is embedded in this asphalt.

■ **coating system**

a number of coats separately applied, in a predetermined order, at suitable intervals to allow for drying and curing, resulting in a completed job.

■ **cobwebbing**

premature drying of a coating during spraying causing a spider web effect.

■ **coefficient of friction**

the quotient of the applied force parallel to a sliding surface required to move an object and its load normal to the sliding surface.

■ **coefficient, dry friction**

a coefficient due to the contact between the moving surfaces associated with a motor shaft.

■ **coefficient, laminar flow**

relates the flow/pressure characteristics of a restrictor at low Reynolds number.

■ **coefficient, minor losses**

relates minor pressure loss with flow velocity and density. The coefficient varies depending on the flow conditions and conduit geometric configuration.

■ **coefficient, orifice flow discharge**

the ratio of the mass flow rate at the discharge end of an orifice to mass flow rate through an ideal orifice, which expands an identical working fluid from the same initial conditions to the same exit pressure.

■ **coefficient, slip flow**

a coefficient proportional to a design characteristic dimension and the cube of the clearance between the internal sealing surfaces.

■ **coefficient, valve pressure-flow**

a coefficient that expresses the ratio of the flow of the valve at maximum opening to the square root of the corresponding maximum pressure.

■ **coefficient, viscous drag**

a coefficient proportional to a characteristic dimension of a bearing divided by the associated clearance.

■ **coffer**

a sunken panel in a ceiling

■ **cofferdam**

a temporary dam built to divert a river around a construction site so the dam can be built on dry ground

■ **cohesion**

the forces which bind the particles of a paint film together into a continuous film.

■ **cold applied**

products that can be applied without heating. These are in contrast to tar or asphalt which need to be heated to be applied.

■ **cold joint**

the interface of newly placed concrete against hardened concrete.

■ **cold mix**

an asphalt which when cold will remain workable for up to 2 weeks. Contains diesel and kerosene. (used for pot holes, general patching, emergency repairs and temporary road reinstatement.)

■ **cold patch**

a roof repair done with cold applied material.

■ **cold planing**

a mechanical method of cold milling a pavement surface to restore the road to a specified grade and profile by removing corrugations, ruts and other surface imperfections in preparation for resurfacing.

■ **cold process built-up roof**

a continuous, semi-flexible roof membrane, consisting of a ply or plies of felts, mats or other reinforcement fabrics that are laminated together with alternate layers of liquid-applied (usually asphalt-solvent based) roof cements or adhesives installed at ambient or a slightly elevated temperature.

■ **cold rolled steel**

low carbon, cold-reduced, sheet steel. Differs from hot rolled steel by the absence of mill scale.

■ **cold working**

the plastic deformation of a metal at a temperature below that at which it recrystallises.

■ **collar**

a conical metal cap flashing used in conjunction with vent pipes or stacks usually located several inches above the plane of the roof, for the purpose of shedding water away from the base of the vent.

■ **collar beam**

nominal 1- or 2-inch-thick members connecting opposite roof

rafters. They serve to stiffen the roof structure.

Collar ties on the left & a beam truss above

■ **collar joint**

the vertical, longitudinal joint between withes of masonry.

■ **collector well**

a well located near a surface water supply used to lower the water table and thereby induce infiltration of surface water through the bed of the water body to the well.

■ **colloids**

quantities of particles small enough to remain suspended in a fluid medium without settling to the bottom.

■ **colour fast**

non-fading.

■ **colour retention**

the ability to retain its original colour during weathering or chemical exposure.

■ **column**

1. a vertical member whose horizontal dimension measured at right angles to the thickness does not exceed three times its thickness.
2. a perpendicular supporting member, circular or rectangular in section, usually consisting of a base, shaft, and capital. In engineering: a vertical structural com-

pression member which supports loads acting in the direction of its longitudinal axis.

■ **combination doors or windows**

combination doors or windows used over regular openings. They provide winter insulation and summer protection and often have self storing or removable glass and screen inserts. This eliminates the need for handling a different unit each season.

■ **combined sewer**

a sewage system that carries both sanitary sewage and strorewater runoff.

■ **combing ridge**

a term used to describe an installation of finishing slate at the ridge of a roof whereby the slates on one side project beyond to the apex of the ridge.

■ **combustible**

capable of burning.

■ **combustible liquid**

any liquid having a flash point at or above 100 F (37.8 C).

■ **commercial quarry**

term that includes open mining for aggregate or limestone for industrial and agricultural purposes.

■ commercial sampling of aggregates or coal

laboratory procedures intended to produce an accuracy such that if a large number of samples are taken from a single lot of aggregates or coal, 95 out of 100 test results will be within + or - 10% of the average of these samples.

■ comminution

the reduction of a rock to progressively smaller particles by natural methods (weathering, erosion, or tectonic movements) or manufacturing processes (breaking, crushing, or grinding by mechanical means).

■ compact rock

a rock so closely grained that no component particles or crystals can be recognised by the eye.

■ compaction

a process of increasing the density of the asphalt by rolling or using other vibrating compactors.

■ compaction curve

the curve showing the relationship between the density (dry unit weight) and the water content of a soil for a given compactive effort.

■ compaction equipment

machines, such as rollers, to expel air from a soil mass and so achieve a high density. smooth-wheel rollers are best for gravels, sands, and gravels-and-clay soils with reasonably high moisture contents. Pneumatic-tired rollers are best for clays with reasonably high moisture content, and sheep foot rollers are the best for clays with low moisture content.

■ compaction test

a basic laboratory compacting procedure to determine the optimum water content at which a soil can be compacted so as to yield the maximum density (dry unit weight). The method involves placing (in a specified manner) a soil sample at a known water content in a mould of given dimensions, subjecting it to a compactive effort of controlled magnitude, and determining the resulting unit weight. The procedure is repeated for various water contents sufficient to establish a relation between water content and unit weight. The maximum dry density for a given compactive effort will usually produce a sample whose saturated strength is near maximum.

■ comparator

an instrument with a calibrated colour wheel used to determine the concentration of various parametres.

■ compatibility

the ability to mix with or adhere properly to other coatings without detriment.

■ **compatible**

two or more substances which can be mixed or blended without separating, reacting, or affecting either material adversely.

■ **compatible materials**

two or more substances that can be mixed, blended, or attached without separating, reacting, or affecting the materials adversely.

■ **compensator control**

a displacement control for variable pumps and motors, which alters their displacement to limit the control parametres.

■ **compliance, hydraulic**

the change in liquid volume under a unit pressure change.

■ **component**

a single hydraulic unit (e.g., a pump, valve, actuator, conduit and fluid) used to perform specific functions.

■ **composite**

a material brought about by combining materials differing in composition or form on a macroscale for the purpose of obtaining specific characteristics and properties. The constituents retain their identity such that they can be physically identified and they exhibit an interface between one another.

■ **composite board**

an insulation board which has two different insulation types laminated together in 2 or 3 layers.

■ **composite construction**

type of construction in which two separate materials act together to resist the applied forces (e.g. concrete deck and steel beams).

■ **composition shingle**

a unit of asphalt shingle roofing.

■ **compost system**

a compost system converts organic waste (food, plant material) into a rich fertiliser. Several commercial models are available that prevent odours and thwart animals.

■ **compost-connected disposal**

a disposal that grinds food waste into a container where it is separated from the water rather than flowing into the waste water system. The contained food waste can then be composted.

■ **compound**

a substance composed of separate elements, ingredients, or parts. Water is a compound made of hydrogen and oxygen.

■ **compounded oil**

a petroleum oil to, which has been added animal or vegetable oil, or other substances.

■ **compounded thermoplastics**

a category of roofing membranes made by blending thermoplastic resins with plasticisers, various modifiers, stabilisers, flame retardants, UV absorbers, fungicides, and other proprietary substances, alloyed with proprietary organic polymers. Some of the membranes listed in this generic category are CPA, EIP, NBP, and TPA.

■ **compressed-air chamber**

the space at the bottom of a caisson into which air is introduced under pressure to exclude water so that excavation can take place

■ **compressibility**

the change in volume of a fluid when pressure is applied. Usually expressed in terms of bulk modulus,, which is the reciprocal of compressibility.

■ **compressibility factor Z**

the product of the pressure and volume of a gas divided by the product of temperature of the gas and the gas constant. This factor can be inserted in the ideal gas law to take into account the departure of true gases from ideal gas behaviour.

■ **compression**

a pressing force that squeezes a material together

■ **compression set**

the inability of a seal to return to its original cross-sectional size and shape after compression. Usually expressed as a percent of original deflection and affects the original mechanical squeeze. It is considered the most important physical characteristic of an O-ring seal.

■ **compressive strength**

the ability of materials and components to resist deformation or other damage caused by the weight of compression of either live or dead loads.

■ **compressor**

a device, which converts mechanical force and motion into pneumatic power.

■ **concealed-nail method**

a method of asphalt roll roofing application in which all nails are driven into the underlying course of roofing and covered by an adhered, overlapping course.

■ **concentration**

amount of material dissolved in a solution; a common unit is mg/L (milligrams of dissolved material in a liter of solution).

■ **concrete**

a mixture of water, sand, small stones, and a gray powder called cement

■ **concrete plain**

concrete either without reinforcement, or reinforced only for shrinkage or temperature changes.

■ **condensate**

the liquid resulting from the condensation of a gas or vapour.

■ **condensation**

1. the deposit of water vapour from the air on any cold surface whose temperature is below the dew point, such as a cold window glass or frame that is exposed to humid indoor air.

2. in a building: beads or drops of water (and frequently frost in extremely cold weather) that accumulate on the inside of the exterior covering of a building when warm, moisture-laden air from the

interior reaches a point where the temperature no longer permits the air to sustain the moisture it holds. Use of louvers or attic ventilators will reduce moisture condensation in attics. A vapour barrier under the gypsum lath or dry wall on exposed walls will reduce condensation in them.

■ **condensation polymerisation**

the formation of polymers by an intermolecular reaction involving at least two monomer species, usually with the production of a low molecular weight by-product such as water.

■ **condition monitoring**

an activity to quantify the properties and parametres of a system or machine in order to determine their condition or fitness for continued service.

■ **conditioning**

the exposure of a material to the influence of a prescribed atmosphere for a stipulated period of time or until a stipulated relation is reached between material and atmosphere.

■ **conductance, thermal**

the thermal transmission in unit time through unit area of a particular body or assembly having defined surfaces, when unit average temperature difference is established between the surfaces.

■ **conduction**

heat transfer through a solid material by contact of one molecule to the next. Heat flows from a higher-temperature area to a lower-temperature one.

■ **conduction band**

the lowest-lying electron energy band that is not completely filled with electrons.

■ **conductor**

a pipe for conveying rain water from the roof gutter to a drain, or from a roof drain to the storm drain; also called a leader, downspout, or down pipe.

■ **conductor head**

a transition component between a through-wall scupper and downspout to collect and direct run-off water.

■ **conduit**

the fluid carrying link between system components.

■ **conduit, electrical**

a pipe, usually metal, in which wire is installed.

■ **confined ground water**

a body of ground water covered by material so impervious as to sever the hydraulic connection with overlying ground water except at the intake. Confined water moves in pressure conduits due to the difference in head between intake and discharge areas of the confined water body.

■ **confirmed**

a water quality issue or problem identified by a river authority as being a confirmed problem or a problem with supporting data.

■ **congruent transformation**

a transformation of one phase to another that does not involve any change in composition.

■ **conical mandrel**

an instrument used to evaluate a coating's resistance to cracking when bent over a specified radius.

■ **connate water**

water (pressure) trapped in the pore spaces of a sedimentary rock at the time it was deposited. It is usually highly mineralised.

■ **connector**

a device for joining a conduit to a component port or to one or more additional conduits.

■ **conservation**

to protect from loss and waste. Conservation of water may mean to save or store water for later use.

■ **construction dry-wall**

a type of construction in which the interior wall finish is applied in a dry condition, generally in the form of sheet materials or wood panelling as contrasted to plaster.

■ **construction joint**

a point where two concrete pours meet. All reinforcement is continuous through the joint.

■ **construction manager**

a person who coordinates the entire construction process and form initial planning and foundation work through the structure's completion.

■ **construction, frame**

a type of construction in which the structural parts are wood or depend upon a wood frame for support. In codes, if masonry veneer is applied to the exterior walls, the classification of this type of construction is usually unchanged.

■ **consumptive use**

consumptive use of water is the quantity of water absorbed by the crop and transpired or used directly in the building of plant tissue together with the water evaporated from the cropped area. It is the quantity of water transpired and evaporated from a cropped area or the normal loss of water from the soil by evaporation and plant transpiration. It is also the quantity of water discharged to the atmosphere or incorporated in the products of the process in connection with vegetative growth, food processing, or an industrial process.

■ **contact cements**

adhesives used to adhere or bond various roofing components. These adhesives adhere mated components immediately on contact of surfaces to which the adhesive has been applied.

■ **contact recreation**

recreational activities involving a significant risk of ingestion of water, including wading by children, swimming, water skiing, diving and surfing.

■ **contaminant**

detrimental matter or energy in a fluid e.g., particulates, moisture, thermal energy, etc.

■ **contaminant lock**

a contaminant induced lockup due to silt lock seizure, coincidence jam and/or formation of an obliterant choke.

■ **contamination**

the deposit, absorption, or adsorption of biological or chemical agents (including the growth of bacteria or fungi) on or by materials, structures, areas, personnel, or objects.

■ **contamination (water)**

damage to the quality of water sources by sewage, industrial waste, or other matter.

■ **contamination control**

an engineering technology involved in planning, organising, and implementing all the activities needed to identify (recognise and describe) contaminant, analyse (characterise and quantify) contaminant, exclude (restrict, isolate, and reject) contaminant, reduce (capture, retain, and remove) contaminant, establish the tolerance of components for contaminant, and ascertain the necessary contaminant balance (between the level of contamination in the fluid and the level of contaminant tolerance of the components to yield a given contaminant service life).

■ **continuity**

means more than being without holes. Because the component that performs the role of the air barrier changes from the wall to the window to the roof, continuity means that all these assemblies must be connected together so as to ensure that there is no break in the air tightness of the envelope.

■ **continuous span beam bridge**

simple bridge made by linking one beam bridge to another; some of the longest bridges in the world are continuous span beam bridges.

■ **contour line**

a line on a map that joins points of equal elevation.

■ **contraction**

thermal action where the size of an object is reduced when cooled; the opposite of expansion.

■ **control**

a method applied to regulate the functions of a component, system or machine.

■ **control joint**

a control joint controls or accommodates movement in the surface component of a roof.

■ **control, servo**

a control actuated by a feed-back system, which compares the output with the reference signal and makes corrections to reduce the difference.

■ **controller**

a component that serves as both a distributor and a regulator. A servovalve is a closed-loop controller; whereas, a proportional control valve is usually used as an open-loop controller.

■ **convection**

a heat transfer process involving motion in a fluid (such as air) caused by the difference in density of the fluid and the action of gravity. Convection affects heat transfer from the glass surface to room air, and between two panes of glass.

■ **cooler**

a heat exchanger used to remove excessive heat from hydraulic fluid.

■ **cooling tower**

a large device mounted on roofs, consisting of many baffles over which water is pumped in order to reduce its temperature.

■ **cooling water load**

the waste heat energy dissipated in the cooling water.

■ **cooling water requirement**

the amount of water needed to pass through the condensing unit. The amount depends on the type of cooling employed and water temperature.

■ **coordination number**

the number of atomic or ionic nearest neighbours.

■ **coping**

the material or masonry units forming a cap or finish on top of a wall, pier, pilaster, chimney, etc. It protects masonry below from penetration of water from above. A construction unit placed at the top of the parapet wall to serve as a cover for the wall.

■ **copolymer**

the product of polymerisation of two or more substances at the same time; a mixed polymer.

■ **corbel**

a shelf or ledge formed by projecting successive courses of masonry out from the face of the wall.

■ **corbel out**

to build out one or more courses of brick or stone from the face of a wall, to form a support for timbers.

■ **core**

a sample taken from the compacted asphalt for testing. Usually for density testing. A small section cut from any material to show internal composition. The core was taken from the roof to verify the construction of the existing roof system. The deck is visible along with the insulation and the roof membrane (see construction section). The core was then replaced and repaired immediately with the appropriate mastic and fibreglass reinforcing mesh.

■ **corner bead**

a strip of formed sheet metal, sometimes combined with a strip of metal lath, placed on corners before plastering to reinforce them. Also, a strip of wood finish three-quarters-round or angular placed over a plastered corner for protection.

■ **corner boards**

used as trim for the external corners of a house or other frame structure against which the ends of the siding are finished.

■ **corner braces**

diagonal braces at the corners of frame structure to stiffen and strengthen the wall.

■ **corner frequency (on a bode plot)**

the frequency at, which the amplitude ratio begins to decrease. It is a measure of the speed of response of the system to an incoming signal the higher the corner frequency, the faster the response.

■ **corner horsepower**

the power required to drive the hydraulic system at full rated pressure and flow. In a hydrostatic transmission it is where the torque and speed are maximum or where the tractive effort and maximum speed of a vehicle intersect.

■ **cornerite**

metal-mesh lath cut into strips and bent to a right angle. Used in interior corners of walls and ceilings on lath to prevent cracks in plastering.

■ **cornice**

a horizontal projecting course on the exterior of a building, usually at the base of the parapet.

■ **cornice return**

that portion of the cornice that returns on the gable end of a house.

■ **corrosion**

the deterioration of metal by chemical or electrochemical reaction resulting from exposure to weathering, moisture, chemicals or other agents or media.

■ **corrugated**

folded or shaped into parallel ridges or furrows so as to form a symmetrically wavy surface.

■ **cost escalation**

change in estimated cost of a project due to inflation, aggravated conditions, etc.

■ **coulomb friction**

friction occurring between sliding surfaces. It is greater just before motion begins than after surfaces are in steady relative motion. The magnitude of Coulomb friction is proportional to the force pressing the surfaces together and is independent of the area of contact and speed (after motion begins).

■ **counter flashing**

a flashing usually used on chimneys at the roofline to cover shingle flashing and to prevent moisture entry.

■ **counterbalance valve**

a valve, which maintains resistance to flow in one direction but permits free flow in the other. It prevents a load from overriding an actuator and falling or dropping..

■ **coupling**

a straight connector for fluid conduits.

■ **course**

1. the term used for each row of shingles of roofing material that forms the roofing, waterproofing, or flashing system;
2. one layer of a series of materials applied to a surface (e.g., a five-course wall flashing is composed of three applications of roof cement with one ply of felt or fabric sandwiched between each layer of roof cement.)

■ **covalent bond**

a primary interatomic bond that is formed by the sharing of electrons between neighboring atoms.

■ **cove**

see **fillet**.

■ **cove moulding**

a moulding with a concave face used as trim or to finish interior corners.

■ **cover**

the clear distance between an exposed concrete surface and the reinforcing bar.

■ **cover plate**

a steel plate attached to a flange of a beam to increase the bending capacity of the member.

■ **coverage**

refers to the area (m²) covered by one ton of asphalt or the volume of seal per square metre.

■ **CPA**

Copolymer Alloy.

■ **CPE**

Chlorinated Polyethylene.

■ **crack**

1. to break so that fissures appear on the surface or through the element; fracture caused by the effects of stress on weak or weakened parts of a member or material.
2. to impair seriously or irreparably.
3. to subject (hydrocarbons) to cracking (to break a large, complex compound into simpler compounds).
4. to break up (chemical compounds) into simpler compounds by means of heat.

■ **crack length**

total outside perimeter of window vent. Used in figuring air infiltration during certification testing.

■ **cracking pressure**

the pressure at which a valve begins to pass fluid.

■ **crashwall**

a wall surrounding the columns of a pier to protect the pier from impact due to an errant vehicle or locomotive.

■ **crasing**

a series of hairline cracks in the surface of weathered materials, having a web-like appearance.

■ **crawl space**

a shallow space below the living quarters of a basement less house, normally enclosed by the foundation wall.

■ **creek**

a small stream of water, which serves as the natural drainage course for a drainage basin of nominal or small size. The term is a relative one as to size, some creeks in the humid section would be called rivers if they occurred in the arid portion.

■ **creep**

the time-dependent permanent deformation that occurs under stress; for most materials it is important only at elevated temperatures.

■ **creosotes**

chemicals used in wood preserving operations and produced by distillation of tar, including polycyclic aromatic hydrocarbons and polynuclear aromatic hydrocarbons (see PAHs and PNAs). contaminating sediments, soils, and surface water, creosotes may cause skin ulcerations and cancer with prolonged exposure.

■ **crest**

the crest is the top of a dam, dike, or spillway, which water must reach before passing over the structure. It is also the summit or highest point of a wave. The highest elevation reached by flood waters flowing in a channel is also called the crest.

■ **CRF**

Condensation Resistance Factor. An indication of a window's ability to resist condensation. The higher the CRF, the less likely condensation is to occur

■ **cricket**

the evaluation of a part of a roof surface as a means of promoting drainage of water from behind an obstacle such as chimney. A small drainage-diverting roof structure of single or double slope placed at the junction of larger surfaces that meet at an angle, such as above a chimney.

■ **criteria**

water quality conditions, which are to be met in order to support and protect desired uses.

■ **critical ground water area**

an area that has certain ground water problems, such as declining water levels. These areas are usually limited in their development and use.

■ **critical low-flow**

low flow conditions below, which some standards do not apply. The impacts of permitted discharges are analysed at critical low-flow.

■ **critical volume reservoir**

a minimal size reservoir having an off-line or on-line configuration. It relies on external fluid conditioning equipment e.g., filtration, heat exchanger, degasser, etc.

■ **crookedness angle**

the angular deflection of the cylinder rod caused by the moment at the sliding connection due to the elasticity of the bearings and seals.

■ **cross frame**

bracing members that are placed in an 'X' or 'K' configuration between girders to assist in the distribution of loads between members. See also, **diaphragms.**

■ **cross section**

a view taken transverse to the longitudinal axis of an element.

■ **cross slope**

the transverse slope of a roadway in section view for the purpose of drainage and/or riding safety.

■ **cross-bridging**

diagonal bracing between adjacent floor joists, placed near the centre of the joist span to prevent joists from twisting.

■ **crosslinked polymer**

a polymer in which adjacent linear molecular chains are joined at various positions by covalent bonds.

■ **crown**

the high point of the roadway (in section view).

■ **crown moulding**

a moulding used on cornice or wherever an interior angle is to be covered.

■ **crushed rock**

an aggregate made from crushed rock, as distinct from crushed gravel.

■ **crystal structure**

for crystalline materials, the manner in which atoms or ions are arrayed in space. It is defined in terms of the unit cell geometry and the atom positions within the cell.

■ **crystal system**

a scheme by which crystal structures are classified according to unit cell geometry.

■ **crystalline**

the state of a solid material characterized by a periodic and repeating three-dimensional arrays of atoms, ions, or molecules.

■ **crystalline waterproofing**

a compound of cement, quartz or silica sand, and other active chemicals that are mixed and packaged for use in a dry powder form; the packaged mixture is then mixed with water and applied to a concrete surface where it penetrates into the pores of concrete.

■ **crystallinity**

for polymers, the state wherein a periodic and repeating atomic arrangement is achieved by molecular chain alignment.

■ **crystallite**

a region within a crystalline polymer in which all the molecular chains are ordered and aligned.

■ **CSPE**

Chlorosulphonated Polyethylene.

■ **cubic foot per second (c.f.s.)**

a unit expressing the rate of discharge of water. One cubic foot per second is equal to the discharge through a rectangular cross section, one foot wide and one foot long, flowing at an average velocity of one foot per second. One cubic foot per second equals 448.8 gallons per minute, and 1.98 acre-feet per day. It is a rate of water movement in volume per time unit.

■ **cubical expansion**

the increase in volume of a substance that accompanies a change in temperature or pressure.

■ **culls**

something rejected, especially as being inferior or worthless, i.e. Masonry units which do not meet the standards or specifications and have been rejected.

■ **culvert**

a structure that carries a water channel through an embankment. Usually constructed of large diameter corrugated steel tubes or precast concrete boxes (Usually with a clear opening of less than 6.2 m).

■ **cupola**

a relatively small roofed structure, generally set on the ridge or peak of a main roof area.

■ **curb**

1. a raised member used to support roof penetrations, such as skylights, mechanical equipment, hatches, etc. above the level of the roof surface.
2. a raised roof perimeter relatively low in height.

■ **cure**

a process whereby a material is caused to form permanent molecular linkages by exposure to chemicals, heat, pressure, and/or weathering.

■ **curie temperature**

that temperature above which a ferromagnetic or ferrimagnetic material becomes paramagnetic.

■ **current**

the portion of a stream or body of water, which is moving with a velocity much greater than the average of the rest of the water. The progress of the water is principally concentrated in the current.

■ **curtain wall as**

exterior non-load bearing wall not wholly supported at each story. Such walls may be anchored to columns, spandrel beams, floors or bearing back-up walls, but not necessarily built between structural elements. Curtain walls must be capable of supporting their own weight for the height of the wall. In contrast, panel walls are required to be self-supporting between stories. Both walls resist lateral forces such as wind pressures and must transfer these forces to adjacent structural members.

■ **curtainwall**

a wall formed above the bridge seat to hide the bearings from view of oncoming traffic. Infrequently used, and only with Uwingwalls (a.k.a. cheekwall).

■ **cushion**

a device built inside the ends of a hydraulic cylinder to control the flow of fluid to the outlet port, thereby slowing the motion of the piston rod and decelerating the load.

■ **cut and cover**

a method of tunnel construction that involves digging a trench, building a tunnel, and then covering it with filth.

■ **cut off**

a piece of roofing membrane consisting of one or more narrow plies of felt usually moped in hot to seal the edge of insulation at the end of a day's work.

■ **cutback**

basic asphalt or tar which has been "cutback" with solvents and oils so that the material become fluid.

■ **cut-back bitumen**

a mixture and a cutter.

■ **cut-in brace**

nominal 2-inch-thick members, usually 2 by 4's, cut in between each stud diagonally.

■ **cutoff**

a permanent detail designed to seal and prevent lateral water movement in an insulation system, and used to isolate sections of a roofing system. (Note A cutoff is different from a tie-off, which may be a temporary or permanent seal.) (See **tie-off.**)

■ **cutout**

the open portions of a strip shingle between the tabs

■ **cutter**

a liquid usually kerosene added to bitumen to reduce it's viscosity. Used in spray seal or for priming.

■ **cycle**

the composition of a predetermined sequence of operations or events of a machine or system, starting and ending at some defined point.

■ **cylinder**

an actuator, which converts pressure energy into linear mechanical force and motion proportional to the effective cross-sectional area of the piston.

■ **cylinder boot**

an accordion shaped boot is installed to protect the piston rod and prevent the ingestion of contaminant across the rod seals.

■ **cylinder, cap end**

the cylinder end closure, which completely covers the bore area. Also called the 'blind end' or 'back end'.

■ **cylinder, double acting**

a cylinder in, which fluid force can be applied to the movable element in either direction.

■ **cylinder, double rod**

a cylinder with a single piston and a piston rod extending from each end.

■ **cylinder, head end**

the cylinder end closure, which covers the differential area between the bore area and the piston rod area. Also referred to as the 'rod end.'

■ **cylinder, tandem**

two or more cylinders having interconnected piston assemblies.

■ **dado**

a rectangular groove across the width of a board or plank. In interior decoration, a special type of wall treatment.

■ **dam**

any artificial barrier, which impounds or diverts water. The dam is generally hydrologically significant if it is 1. 25 feet or more in height from the natural bed of the stream and has a storage of at least 15 acre-feet. 2. Or has an impounding capacity of 50 acre-feet or more and is at least six feet above the natural bed of the stream.

■ **dam failure**

catastrophic event characterised by the sudden, rapid, and uncontrolled release of impounded water.

■ **damage repair**

damaged composite structures can be repaired by several available techniques. For a thermoplastic structural assembly, a section or plug can be filled to the damaged area consisting of a previously processed multi-ply thermoplastic. A hole is drilled through the centre to contain interior and exterior plates which exert pressure on the section while it is locally heated, causing resin flow and reconsolidation. With a highly loaded composite structure, it is necessary to match me stiffness of the surrounding material because a stiffer patch material, such as a steel or titanium splice plate, can pick up more load, change the load path and put a greater stress on the adjacent structure. In addition, galvanic corrosion can be a problem; when pairing together carbon and aluminium, it is necessary to employ a layer of resin or glass fibre for separation.

■ **damage resistance**

principal factors include impact resistance (toughness) and abrasion resistance.

■ damp proof course (DPC)

resistance to the movement of moisture from the ground (or the lower part of the structure) to the upper part through capillarity.

■ damp proofing

prevention of moisture penetration by capillary action. It is achieved by application of materials or by the treatment of surfaces in order to stop (rarely) or to retard the passage of moisture. It allows evaporation from the inside of the building.

■ damper

a device used to restrict the amplitude of a shock wave or the movement of a mechanical part as a function of velocity.

■ damping

hysteresis, or variations in properties resulting from dynamic loading conditions. Damping is related to the fundamental visco elastic mechanisms of polymers and is characteristic of the plastic as fabricated, the frequency of loading, and the stress. It provides a mechanism for dissipating energy during deformation of a material, without excessive temperature rise, preventing premature brittle fracture and improving fatigue performance.

■ damping coefficient

the proportional quantity that relates the resisting force to its velocity in any type of motion.

■ damping length

the horizontal distance between the centres of the incoming and outgoing flows in a spool valve. It is used in the transient flow force analysis. Take positive sign if the fluid flows outward at the metering orifice and negative sign otherwise.

■ damping ratio

the ratio of the actual damping in the system to that damping, which would produce critical damping.

■ dampproofing

treatment of a surface or structure to resist the passage of water in the absence of hydro-static pressure..

■ dap

a notch out in the bottom of a prestressed concrete beam to provide a level surface to rest on the bearing.

■ DAPM

The Data Acquisition Program Manager.

■ datum

all ground surface elevations are measured from a certain point called a datum.

■ daylighting strategies

these are methods that use natural light to full advantage to minimise the need for artificial lighting during the day. For example a clerestory is a daylighting strategy that allows natural light into a building interior through a raised section of roof with vertical glass. Shading of the glass allows light in while minimising heat gain. Louvers on the exterior of vertical glass on a house can reflect natural light into the interior without the excessive heat gain associated with harsh, direct sunlight. Horizontal light shelves, located high on a wall with glass above (and possibly below) and projecting into the interior and typically to the exterior as well, are excellent devices for bouncing daylight deep into a room.

■ **DCP (data collection platform)**

an electronic device that connects to a river or rainfall gauge that records data from the gauge and at pre-determined times transmits that data through a satellite to a remote computer.

■ **dead band**

the region or band of no response and where an error signal will not cause a corresponding actuation of the controlled variable.

■ **dead level**

essentially horizontal or flat, as in a roof deck or rooftop with no intentional slope to the roof drains. Also referred to as zero (0) slope.

■ **dead loads**

permanent non-moving loads that result from the weight of a building's structural and architectural components, mechanical and electrical equipment, and the roof assembly itself. Essentially the same as 'dead weight' or 'dead weight loads'.

■ **deadman**

an anchor set behind a tie-back retaining wall. The anchor must be set outside of the failure zone.

■ **decay**

disintegration of wood or other substance through the action of fungi,

■ **deceleration**

the negative rate of change of velocity per unit time.

■ **deciduous**

trees and plants that shed their leaves at the end of the growing season.

■ **deck**

a structural component of the roof of a building. The deck must be capable of safely supporting the design dead and live loads, including the weight of the roof systems, and the additional live loads required by the governing building codes. Decks are either non-combustible (e.g., corrugated metal, concrete, or gypsum) or combustible (e.g., wood plank or plywood), and provide the substrate to which the roofing or waterproofing system is applied.

■ **deck paint**

an enamel with a high degree of resistance to mechanical wear, designed for use on such surfaces as porch floors.

■ **decompression**

the release of fluid under pressure.

deep strength asphalt pavement

a pavement structure in which the wearing course and a substantial portion of the base consist of asphalt.

deflect

to bend or deform under weight.

deflection

the vertical movement of a pavement under load. This is often measured to determine the pavement life and existing wear rate of the pavement, and can determine rehabilitation programmes.

deflection (bowing, sagging)

the downward displacement of a structural member or system under load.

deform

to change shape.

deformed bars

a reinforcing bar with 'bumps' on the surface to improve the mechanical connection between the bar and the concrete.

degradation

a deleterious change in the chemical structure, physical properties, or appearance of a material due to natural or artificial exposure (e.g., exposure to radiation, moisture, heat, freezing, wind, ozone, oxygen, etc.).

degree

the exponent of the highest order derivative, after the equation has been cleared of fractions and radicals in the dependent variable and its derivatives.

dehydration

the removal of water and moisture from the hydraulic fluid.

deionised water

ions are removed from the water so as to not interfere with chemical reactions; also called DI water.

delamination

cracks or voids below and parallel to a concrete surface that cause the concrete to peel off in layers.

delivery

the volume of fluid discharged per unit time by a pump or other component in a system.

delta

an alluvial deposit made of rock particles (sediment and debris) dropped by a stream as it enters a body of water.

dense graded mix

an asphalt produced with aggregate that produces a continual grading. Usually low air voids as compared with open graded products.

density

the mass of substance in a unit volume. When expressed in the metric system, it is numerically equal to the specific gravity of the same substance.

dependability

the ability of a component or system to remain functional during a definite period of time under specific operational conditions.

■ **dependent variable**

a variable quantity of a system whose value depends upon some other variable quantity or quantities.

■ **deposit**

something dropped or left behind by moving water, as sand or mud.

■ **depth filters**

a filter medium, which primarily retains contaminant within its tortuous passages.

■ **derivative**

the rate of change of a variable with respect to the change of another variable.

■ **derivative action**

a control operation in, which the speed with, which a correction is made is proportional to the rate of change of the deviation from the established limits.

■ **derivative, partial**

a derivative taken with respect to a single independent variable while all remaining independent variables are treated as constants.

■ **desalinisation**

the process of salt removal from sea or brackish water.

■ **design life**

is an important quantitative measure that defines the quality of the project. Buildings will not last forever. The owner and designer should establish a reasonable design life for each project. This requires consideration of the economic factors such as initial cost and maintenance costs. The design life will have an impact on the selection of materials, maintenance procedures, and the selected factors of safety. The expected performance is also an important qualitative measure for the design of the project. The minimum performance level is set by the building code, however, there are aspects of a structural brick veneer system performance that are not explicitly covered by the code and require judgment.

It has been useful to define two distinct levels of expected life and performance:

level 1 (institutional) is intended to signify a high level of quality and long life. Buildings of this type might include public or institutional buildings. Specifically, these are buildings where the additional costs associated with higher quality are judged to be necessary in meeting the overall project requirements.

level 2 (commercial) is intended to signify a good level of quality and an average design life. Buildings of this type might include general office, industrial, and residential buildings. These are buildings where the additional cost of level 1 (institutional) quality is not economically justified or necessary. The primary difference in design life is obtained by increasing the quality of the connectors, improving the weather resistance of the materials and expanding on the amount of inspection and testing.

■ **detent**

a device, which locks a valve spool in selected positions. Also see **'hydraulic detent'**.

■ **detergent**

in lubrication, it is an additive or a compounded lubricant having the property of keeping insoluble matter in suspension so that is not deposited where it can do harm. It can also redisperse deposits already formed.

■ **deterioration**

an item or element, subject to degradation or having a limited life which cannot be renewed, is considered serviceable while stored (see also storage life). Deterioration implies the impairment of usefulness or value.

■ **deuterium**

a form of hydrogen atom in, which the nucleus contains one proton and one neutron. About .0150/0 of all hydrogen atoms have such nuclei. Deuterium, also called heavy hydrogen, is the hydrogen in heavy water.

■ **devitrification**

the process in which a glass (noncrystalline or vitreous solid) transforms to a crystalline solid.

■ **dew**

the droplets of water condensed from adjacent air when the temperature falls.

■ **dew point**

1. the critical temperature at which vapour condenses from the atmosphere and forms water.

2. temperature at which a vapour begins to deposit as a liquid. Applies especially to water in the atmosphere.

■ **dew point temperature**

the temperature at which water vapour condenses in cooling air at the existing atmospheric pressure and vapour content. Cooling at or below the dew point will cause condensation.

■ **dewwater**

to remove water from wastes, soils, or chemicals.

■ **diagram, cutaway**

a drawing showing the principle internal parts of components, controls and actuating mechanisms, interconnecting passages and functions of individual components.

■ **diagram, pictorial**

a drawing showing each component in its actual shape according to the manufacturer's installation.

■ **diagram, schematic or graphical**

a drawing showing each piece of apparatus including all interconnecting lines by means of approved standard symbols.

■ **diamagnetism**

a weak form of induced or nonpermanent magnetism for which the magnetic susceptibility is negative.

■ **diaphragm**

bracing that spans between bridge main beams or girders that assist in the distribution of loads. Also, transverse members in a closed box member.

■ dielectric

any material that is electrically insulating.

■ dielectric constant

the ratio of the permittivity of a medium to that of a vacuum.

■ dielectric strength

the magnitude of an electric field necessary to cause significant current passage through a dielectric material.

■ differential area

the net difference between two areas.

■ differential equation

an equation, which involves one or more derivatives. They are classified as Ordinary Differential Equations and Partial Differential Equations.

■ differential pressure

the net effect of two different pressures acting on separate areas or at different points in a system or component.

■ diffusion

mass transport by atomic motion.

■ diffusion coefficient

the constant of proportionality between diffusion flux and the concentration gradient in Fick's first law.

■ digital

a term pertaining to the general class of devices, components, or circuits whose output varies in discrete steps (i.e., pulses or "on-off" characteristics).

■ digital computer

a computer that works with discrete numbers and can only give the answer to one specific arithmetic problem at a time.

■ dillo dirt

this is the name of the composted, sludge produced from Austin's wastewater and yard waste. It is a rich fertiliser marketed for use in landscapes - not vegetable gardens.

■ dilution

process of adding a known amount of a solvent (usually water) to another solution to make it less concentrated. This is often done when working with faecal coliform samples to ensure proper and readable colony development.

■ dimensional stability

the ability of a material to resist change in length, width, and/or thickness that results from exposure to elevated or freezing temperatures, and moisture, over time.

■ dipole (electric)

a pair of equal yet opposite electrical charges that are separated by a small distance

■ direct flood damage

the damage done to property, structures, goods, etc., by a flood as measured by the cost of replacement and repairs.

■ **direct nailing**

to nail perpendicular to the initial surface or to the junction of the pieces joined. Also termed face nailing.

■ **direct runoff**

the runoff entering stream channels promptly after rainfall or snowmelt. Superposed on base runoff, it forms the bulk of the hydrograph of a flood.

■ **directional valve**

a valve, which directs or prevents the flow of fluid to specific sections of a circuit.

■ **discharge**

in the simplest form, discharge means outflow of water. The use of this term is not restricted as to course or location and it can be applied to describe the flow of water from a pipe or from a drainage basin. If the discharge occurs in a course or channel, it is correct to speak of the discharge of a canal or of a river. It is also correct to speak of the discharge of a canal or stream into a lake, stream or ocean. Discharge is a comprehensive outflow term. Other words related to it are runoff, stream flow and yield.

■ **discharge curve**

a curve that expresses the relation between the discharge of a stream or open conduit.

■ **discharge of ground water**

occurs when water flows out from underground.

■ **discharge permit**

a permit issued by the state to discharge effluent into waters of the state.

■ **discontinuity**

a point at, which the relationship between the independent variable and the dependent variable changes; i.e., the point where a function is not mathematically continuous.

■ **dishwasher**

the proper use of automatic dishwashers can save water compared to hand washing (up to 37%) and may also use less energy, depending on your style of hand washing.

■ **dislocation**

a linear crystalline defect around which there is an atomic misalignment.

■ **dispersancy**

the ability of a fluid to disperse materials in the form of minute particles throughout the base fluid.

■ **dispersant**

In lubrication, it is synonymous and used interchangeably with detergent.

■ **displacement**

the volume of fluid, which can pass through a pump, motor or cylinder in a given time or during a single actuation event; e.g., revolution or stroke.

■ **dissipative load**

a load that must be overcome to achieve motion stiction or static friction, coulomb friction, viscous friction, and windage.

■ dissolve

a condition where solid particles mix, molecule by molecule with a liquid, and appear to become part of the liquid.

■ dissolved oxygen

the amount of oxygen dissolved in water or sewage. Concentrations of less than 5 parts per million can limit aquatic life or cause offensive odours. Low DO is generally due to excessive organic matter present in water as a result of inadequate waste treatment and runoff from agricultural or urban land.

■ dissolved solids

the total amount of dissolved inorganic material contained in water or wastes. Excessive dissolved solids make water unsuitable for drinking or industrial uses.

■ distillation

the separation of different substances in a solution by boiling off those of low boiling point first. For example, water can be distilled and the steam condensed back into a liquid that is almost pure water. The impurities (minerals) remain in the concentrated residue.

■ distributed parameter model

a mathematical model having an infinite degree of freedom in, which the variables can act over the entire length of the system elements. The converse is a lumped model.

■ distribution of water

the management of water, which allows water users to receive the amount of water to, which they are entitled by law and as supply permits.

■ dither

a relatively high frequency, low amplitude periodic signal or oscillatory motion sometimes superimposed on the servovalve input to improve system resolution. The dither (either mechanically or hydraulically) is applied to offset friction (static friction or silt lock), promote rapid and accurate response, and/or improve system resolution.

■ diversion

in the most simple term it means to remove water from a water body. It can also mean individually designed diversions across a hillside. They may be used to protect bottomland from hillside runoff, divert water away from active gullies, or protect buildings from runoff.

■ diversion channel

a bypass created to divert water around a dam so that construction can take place

■ DL

Dead Load. Permanent loads due to known sources such as the weight of the concrete deck, girders, diaphragms, utilities, etc.

■ DO

Dissolved Oxygen.

■ **dog's tooth**

brick laid with their corners projecting from the wall face.

■ **dome**

a curved roof enclosing a circular space; a three-dimensional arch.

■ **domestic consumption (use)**

water used for household purposes such as washing, food preparation and showers. It is the quantity, or quantity per capita, of water consumed in a municipality or district for domestic uses or purposes during a given period. It sometimes encompasses all uses, including the quantity wasted, lost, or otherwise unaccounted for.

■ **doorjamb, interior**

the surrounding case into which and out of which a door closes and opens. It consists of two upright pieces, called side jambs, and a horizontal head jamb.

■ **doping**

the intentional alloying of semiconducting materials with controlled concentrations of donor or acceptor impurities.

■ **dormer**

an opening in a sloping roof, the framing of which projects out to form a vertical wall suitable for windows or other openings. The house-like structure which projects from a sloping roof.

■ **double seal**

a seal coat (refer seal) consisting of two successive applications.

■ **double tee**

refers usually to a pre cast roof deck panel poured with two fins in its underside to impart flexural rigidity.

■ **double-acting**

describes a component such as a cylinder, which operates in two directions or where an actuating force can be applied in either direction.

■ **dowel**

a reinforcing bar that connects one pour of concrete to another. It may also act as a lap splicing bar to avoid having long reinforcing bars sticking out of a pour.

■ **downspout**

a conduit used to carry runoff water from a scupper, conductor head, or gutter of a building to a lower roof level, or to the ground or storm water runoff system..).

■ **downstation**

in the direction of decreasing survey station values

■ **downstream face**

the side of the dam that is not against the water.

■ **drain**

a passage, which returns fluid from a component to a lower pressure region such as a reservoir and should normally enter the reservoir below the fluid level.

■ **drainage basin**

an area in, which water drains in to a stream system.

■ **drainage density**

the number of watercourses per unit of land area.

■ **drainage water**

the water, which has been collected by a drainage system. It may come from surface water or from water passing through the soil. It may be of a quality suitable for reuse or it may be of no further economic use.

■ **drains**

systems to control water tables near the ground surface to maintain levels at or below specified depths.

■ **drawdown**

the lowering of the water level caused by pumping. It is measured in feet for a given quantity of water pumped during a specified period, or after the pumping level has become constant.

■ **drawing**

a deformation technique used to fabricate metal wire and tubing. Deformation is accomplished by pulling the material through a die by means of a tensile force applied on the exit side.

■ **drawing detail**

a top view drawing, of a building or roof showing the roof perimeter and indicating the projections and roof mounted equipment, drawn to scale.

■ **drawing outline**

a top view drawing, of a building or roof showing only the perimeter drawn to scale.

■ **dressed and matched**

boards or planks machined in such a matter that there is a groove on one edge and a corresponding tongue on the other.

■ **drier**

the section of the plant that heats and dries the aggregate.

■ **drier paint**

usually oil-soluble soaps of such metals as lead manganese, or cobalt, which, in small proportions, hasten the oxidation and hardening (drying) of the drying oils in paints.

■ **drift**

the change of a parameter with time under steady state operating conditions.

■ **drilled shaft**

see **caisson**.

■ **drilling mud**

a mixture of clay and water that is forced through a rotating bit when drilling a well in consolidated and unconsolidated strata. The same term is used when drilling in bedrock.

■ **drip**

1. a member of a cornice or other horizontal exterior finish course that has a projection beyond the other parts for throwing off water. A groove under a sill or drip cap to cause water to drop off on the outer edge instead of drawing back and running down the face of the building.
2. a projecting piece of material, such as a fin or a groove, installed at the outer edge of a sill, or soffit, and shaped to interrupt the flow of water downward or and prevent its running down the face of any vertical surface or inward across the soffit.

■ **drip cap**

a moulding placed on the exterior top side of a door or window frame to cause water to drip beyond the outside of the frame.

■ **drip edge**

a metal flashing, or other overhanging component, with an outward projecting lower edge, intend-ed to control the direction of dripping water and help protect underlying building components. A drip edge also can be used to break the continuity of contact between the roof perimeter and wall components to help prevent capillary action.)

■ **drip page**

bitumen material that drips through roof deck joints, or over the edge of a roof deck.

■ **drop spillway**

an overfall structure in, which water drops over a vertical wall onto a protected apron at a lower elevation.

■ **droplet**

leakage defined as a non-falling fluid particle.

■ **drought**

there is no universally accepted quantitative definition of drought. Generally, the term is applied to periods of less than average precipitation over a certain period of time; nature's failure to fulfill the water wants and needs of man.

■ **dry lap**

a term describing the absence of bitumen between the plies of felt at the overlap in a burm.

■ **dry sheet**

a ply mechanically attached to wood or gypsum decks to prevent asphalt or pitch from penetrating the deck and leaking into the building below.

■ **drywall**

interior covering material, such as gypsum board or plywood, which is applied in large sheets or panels.

■ **duct**

a cylindrical or rectangular 'tube' used to move air either from exhaust or intake. The installation is referred to as 'duct work'.

■ **ductility**

a measure of a material's ability to undergo appreciable plastic deformation before fracture.

■ **ducts**

in a house, usually round or rectangular metal pipes for distributing warm air from the heating plant to rooms, or air from a conditioning device or as cold air returns. Ducts are also made of asbestos and composition materials.

■ **durability**

1. able to exist for a long time without significant deterioration.
2. designed to be durable, such as in 'durable goods'.
3. the ability of resisting agents or influences which tend to cause changes, decay, or dissolution. Durability is not an intrinsic property of a material but depends largely on how a material reacts to a specific environment such as moisture, temperature, ultra-violet radiation, and to the presence of other materials (incompatibility). A material also often sees two different environments during its service life, one during construction and another after the building has been completed. The environment the air barrier sees only briefly during construction may nonetheless be detrimental to the long term performance of some of the materials that compose it.

These materials should always therefore be adequately protected from rain, heat, ultra-violet radiation, cold, and mechanical damage during construction

■ **duty cycle**

a reflection of the work cycle on the individual components of the system.

■ **dwell**

the portion of a stroke or cycle in, which the feed or pressure stroke is stopped in one part of the system.

■ **dynamic load**

any load which is non-static, such as a wind load or a moving live load.

■ **dynamite**

a blasting explosive, based on nitroglycerin, but much safer to handle than nitroglycerin alone.

■ **e1/e2**

ratio of virtual eccentricities occurring at the ends of a column or wall under design. The absolute value is always less than or equal to 1.0.

■ **earth sheltered design**

design of houses that are partially or totally below ground, either as a result of digging into existing topography or filling over parts of the structure. Earth sheltered design uses the constant temperature of the soil to improve energy efficiency, and can' beneficial for use of hilly sites by decreasing maintenance and environmental impact.

■ **earth's thermal energy**

a short distance below the surface, the Earth maintains a mostly constant temperature reasonably close to human comfort range. This can be used advantageously by certain heating and cooling systems. The higher temperatures found in the Earth are also used for producing electricity in some areas.

■ **eave**

the part of a roof which projects out from the side wall, or the lower edge of the part of a roof that overhangs a wall.

■ **eave height**

the vertical dimension from finished grade to the eave.

■ **EBW**

abbreviation for Electron Beam Welding

■ **eccentric load**

a compressive or tensile load which does not act through the centroid of the cross section.

■ **eccentricity**

the ratio of the difference between the maximum and minimum wall thickness expressed as a percentage. The distance of the line of action of the load from the centroid. The measure of a misalignment or being off-centre.

■ **ech**

polyepichlorohydrin, commonly referred to as epichlorohydrin. (See **epichlorohydrin**.)

■ **edge metal**

a term relating to brake or extruded metal around the perimeter of a roof.

■ **edge stripping**

membrane flashing strips cut to specific widths used to seal/flash perimeter edge metal and the roof membrane.

■ **edge venting**

the practice of providing regularly spaced or continuously protected (e.g., louvered) openings along a roof edge or perimeter, used as part of a ventilation system to dissipate heat and moisture vapour.

■ **eductor**

this is a liquid jet pump, which uses a high velocity liquid jet to produce motive power for boosting the flow to the hydraulic pump.

■ **effective height**

the height of a member to be assumed for calculating the slenderness ratio.

■ **effective length of rod**

the distance between the load application point and the cylinder resistance point.

■ **effective porosity**

the portion of pore space in saturated permeable material where the movement of water takes place.

■ **effective precipitation (rainfall)**

the part of precipitation, which produces runoff; a weighted average of current and antecedent precipitation 'effective' in correlating with runoff. It is also that part of the precipitation falling on an irrigated area, which is effective in meeting the requirements of consumptive use.

■ **effective thickness**

the thickness of a member to be assumed for calculating the slenderness ratio.

■ **efficiency**

the ratio of output to input power of a single unit or a whole system usually expressed as a percent.

■ **efficiency, hydraulic**

this efficiency is defined as the actual head produced by a centrifugal pump to its ideal head.

■ **efficiency, mechanical**

the ratio of the overall efficiency to the volumetric efficiency.

■ **efficiency, overall or operating**

the ratio of horsepower out to the horsepower in or the product of the volumetric efficiency and the mechanical efficiency.

■ **efficiency, volumetric**

the ratio of the actual output at a given pressure to the theoretical output determined by the geometrical displacement.

■ **efficient fixtures and appliances**

fixtures and appliances that use the least amount of energy and water and accomplish tasks are considered efficient.

■ **efflorescence**

a powder or stain sometimes found on the surface of masonry, because mortar must be wet to render it plastic for bricklaying, brickwork becomes damp in the course of construction. It subsequently dries, the moisture, in which the various salts derived from mortar and bricks have been dissolved, moves to the wall surface to evaporate, leaving a deposit of salts, usually as a white coating on the bricks resulting from deposition of water-soluble salts. the process by which water leeches soluble salts out of concrete or mortar and deposits them on the surface. Also used as the name for these deposits.

■ **effluents**

something that flows out, usually a polluting gas or liquid discharge.

■ **elastance loads**

a load analogous to that produced by a spring when stretched, it tries to contract, and vice versa as given by Hooke's law.

■ **elastic deformation**

displacements that occur within the elastic range of a member, where the member returns to its original undeformed shape when the load is removed.

■ **elastic modulus**

see **modulus of elasticity**.

■ **elasticity**

the property of matter by virtue of which it tends to return to its original size and shape after removal of a stress or force which caused a deformation.

■ **elastomer**

an elastic, rubber-like material (such as rubber or plastic) having elastic properties. At room temperature, it can be stretched to twice its original length and will snap back to its original length upon release. Used for seals, hoses and special enclosures.

■ **elastomeric**

the elastic, rubber-like properties of a material that will stretch when pulled and will return relatively quickly to its original shape when released.

■ **elastomeric coating**

a coating system which, when fully cured, is capable of being stretched at least twice its original length (100% elongation) and recovering to its original dimensions.

■ **electric arc furnace slag**

refer slag.

■ **electrical engineer**

an engineer concerned with electrical devices and systems and with the use of electrical energy.

■ **electrodylasis**

a process, which uses an electrical current and an arrangement of permeable membranes to separate soluble minerals from water. It is often used to desalinise salt or brackish water.

■ **electro-hydraulic**

a component, which converts an electric signal into a hydraulic signal.

■ **electromagnetic fields (EMFs)**

electric and magnetic fields are common in nature and in all living things. Electric power produces fields that have a possible association with health risks. Continuing health risk evaluation is occurring, but avoiding excessive exposure to EMFs is recommended. Placing electric metres and panels on walls of least occupied areas is a simple method to minimise exposure to EMFs.

■ **electromagnetic vulnerability**

the characteristics of a system that cause it to suffer a definite degradation (incapability to perform the designated mission) as a result of having been subjected to a certain level of electromagnetic effects.

■ **electronegativity**

for an atom, having a tendency to accept valence electrons.

■ **elevation**

the distance that any point on the ground is above a certain point called a datum.

■ **elongation**

the ability of a material (e.g., roofing membrane) to be stretched by the application of a force.

■ **embankment dam**

a dam composed of a mound of earth and rock; the simplest type of gravity dam.

■ **embedment**

1. the process of installing or pressing-in a reinforcement felt, fabric, mat or panel uniformly into bitumen or adhesive.
2. the process of pressing granules into coating during the manufacture of factory-pre-pared roofing.
3. the process whereby ply sheet, aggregate, or other roofing components settle into hot- or cold-applied bitumen via the force of gravity.

■ **embodied energy**

this is the energy invested in bringing a product or material into existence.

■ **embrittlement**

the loss of flexibility or elasticity of a material. The transition of a flexible material to a brittle state.

■ **empowerment**

act by which an employee, contractor or consultant is given the necessary freedom to make full use of his knowledge, energies and judgement to provide better service. It necessarily involves freedom of and responsibility for decision-making.

■ **emulsion**

is a mixture of water and bitumen used for priming, sealing and tack coating of asphalt layers. In roofing, a coating consisting of asphalt and fillers suspended in water.

■ **emulsion, water-oil**

a stabilised mixture of two immiscible components, water and oil, and may contain additives. There are two types: oil-in-water and water-in-oil.

■ **enbloc manifold**

it is a manifold machined from a solid block of metal and often contains a large number of control elements interconnected by drilled passages.

■ **enclosure**

a housing for a hydraulic apparatus.

■ **end lap**

the distance of overlap where one ply, panel, or piece extends beyond the end of the immediately adjacent underlying ply, panel, or piece.

■ **energy**

in scientific terms, the ability or capacity of doing work. Various forms of energy include kinetic, potential, thermal, nuclear, rotational, and electromagnetic. One form of energy may be changed to another, as when coal is burned to produce steam to drive a turbine, which produces electric energy.

■ **energy efficient lighting**

motion sensors and photo switches activate the exterior lights only when needed. Energy efficient bulbs and reflectors reduce the energy when lit in exterior and interior locations.

■ **energy recovery ventilator (erv)**

draws stale air from the house and transfers the heat or coolness in that air to the fresh air being pulled into the house. This can help reduce energy costs and dilute indoor pollutants.

■ **engineered brick masonry**

masonry which is designed by structural analysis methods.

■ **engineered wood**

relatively new term that means just what it says: wood products that are engineered. Plywood is considered to be the original engineered wood product and has been used for structural applications since the 1940s. Since then, other products have been developed which fit into the engineered wood family: *Glulam*, *Osb*, and wood joists are some that are represented by APA and EWS. Glued engineered wood products, including plywood, oriented strand board (osb), Glued Laminated Timber (*Glulam*), wood joists and structural composite lumber are manufactured by bonding together wood strands, veneers, lumber or other wood fibre to form a larger, more efficient composite structural unit.

These products are extremely resource efficient because they utilise more of the available resource with minimal waste. In addition, in many cases, they are produced using faster growing and often under utilised wood species from managed forests and tree farms, thus reducing the industry's reliance on so-called 'old growth' forests. At the same time, glued engineered wood products meet marketplace needs for products with superior and consistent performance characteristics. For example, *Glulam* beams and wood i-joists, 'engineered' to exacting standards, can carry greater loads over longer spans than is possible with an equivalent size of solid sawn wood.

■ **engineering**

a profession in which a knowledge of math and natural science is applied to develop ways to utilise the materials and forces of nature for the benefit of all human beings.

■ **engineering ceramics**

technical ceramics for structural applications.

■ **enrichment seal**

an application of spraying a bituminous material of either bitumen and kerosene bituminous emulsion or formed bitumen to an existing surface to improve the bonding of the binder and the aggregates (refer **spray seal reference chart**).

■ **envelope (bitumen-stop)**

a continuous edge seal formed at the perimeter and at penetrations by extending the base sheet or one ply of felt beyond the edge of the membrane field plies. After all overlying field plies or insulation are in place, the extended ply is turned back onto the membrane and adhered. The envelope is intended to prevent bitumen seepage from the edge of the membrane.

■ **environment**

an organism's surroundings. Water is a major part of an organism's surroundings in many instances.

■ **EPDM**

Ethylene Propylene Dine Monomer. A single ply membrane consisting of synthetic rubber; usually 45 or 60 mils. Application can be ballasted, fully adhered or mechanically attached.

■ **epichlorohydrin (ECH)**

a synthetic rubber including two epichlorohydrin based elastomers. It is similar to and compatible with EPDM. ECH is typically used in lieu of EPDM when enhanced resistance to animal fat or other oils is needed.

■ **epoxy**

a class of synthetic, thermosetting resins that produce tough, hard, chemical-resistant coatings and adhesives.

■ **epoxy-coated reinforcing bar**

Reinforcing steel coated with a thin film of epoxy. Used to prevent corrosion of the bar.

■ **equation of state**

a mathematical expression defining the physical state of a substance (gas, liquid, or solid) by relating volume to pressure and to absolute temperature for a given mass of the substance.

■ **equilibrium moisture content (EMC)**

1. the moisture content of a material stabilised at a given temperature and relative humidity, expressed as percent moisture by weight;
2. the typical moisture content of a material in any given geographical area.

■ **equivalent length**

an expression for pressure loss of fittings and conduit interruptions in terms of equivalent length of a straight conduit of specified diameter.

■ **equiviscous temperature**

the temperature at which a bitumen attains the proper viscosity for built-up membrane application.

■ **equiviscous temperature application range**

the recommended bitumen application temperature range. The range is approximately 25°F (14°C) above or below the EVT, thus giving a range of approximately 50°F (28°C). The EVT Range Temperature is measured in the mop cart or mechanical spreader just prior to application of the bitumen to the substrate.

■ **erosion**

the wearing away of the land surface by wind, water, ice or other geologic agents. Erosion occurs naturally from weather or runoff but is often intensified by human land use practices.

■ **error**

the difference between the desired parameter value and the actual parameter value.

■ **error signal**

the signal, which is the algebraic summation of an input signal and a feedback signal.

■ **estuaries**

an area where fresh water meets salt water; for example, bays, mouths of rivers, salt marshes, and lagoons.

■ **ethylene interpolymers**

a group of thermoplastic compounds generally based on PVC polymers from which certain single-ply roofing membranes can be formulated.

■ **ethylene propylene diene terpolymer**

designated nomenclature of ASTM for a terpolymer of ethylene, propylene, and a diene. EPDM material is a thermosetting synthetic elastomer.

■ **eutectic phase**

one of the two phases found in the eutectic structure.

■ **eutrophication**

the process of enrichment of waterbodies by nutrients. Eutrophication of a lake normally contributes to its slow evolution into a bog or marsh and ultimately to dry land. Eutrophication may be accelerated by human activities and thereby speed up the aging process.

■ **evaporation**

the process by, which water becomes a vapour at a temperature below the boiling point.

■ **evaporation pond**

a containment area where liquids are allowed to evaporate. In some cases a spraying mechanism is used to speed evaporation.

■ **EVT**

Equiviscous Temperature

■ **exclusion device**

a sealing device designed to exclude environmental contaminants from the internal parts of a hydraulic cylinder.

■ **exhaust ventilation**

air that is typically vented or exhausted from the roof cavity, typically through vents installed on the upslope portion of the roof. For example, with most steep-slope roof assemblies exhaust vents are typically located at or near the ridge.

■ **exodermic deck**

a lightweight decking system consisting of a grid of closely spaced parallel steel ribs and a precast concrete topping.

■ **exotherm**

heat generated by a chemical reaction.

■ **expansion**

the elongation of a superstructure due to temperature increases or release of camber in a beam.

■ **expansion cleat**

a cleat designed to handle thermal movement of the metal roof panels.

■ **expansion coefficient**

the amount that a specific material will vary in any one dimension with a change of temperature.

■ **expansion joint**

a device used to make up the motion of expansion and contraction. On large roofs this provision for the movement of the materials forming the walls, roof deck and roof covering is usually made by deliberately separating the building into sections, and covering separation between adjacent sections with the expansion joint to allow movement but keep out the weather. Expansion joints, unlike control joints, penetrate through the roof deck.

■ **exposure**

the condition of being unprotected, especially from severe weather or generally, the condition of being subject to some effect or influence.

■ **exterior grade plywood**

exterior grade plywood uses phenol formaldehyde as an adhesive, which outgasses in much smaller amounts compared to urea formaldehyde,, which is used in interior grade plywood and particle board.

■ **extrinsic semiconductor**

a semi-conducting material for which the electrical behaviour is determined by impurities.

■ **extrusion**

an item formed by forcing a base metal (frequently aluminium) or plastic, at a malleable temperature, through a die to achieve a desired shape.

■ **eyebrow**

a flat, normally concrete, projection which protrudes horizontally from a building wall; eyebrows are generally located above windows.

■ **fabric**

a material constructed of interlaced yarns, fibres, or filaments, usually a planar structure. Nonwovens are sometimes included in this classification.

■ **fabric batch**

fabric woven from one warp loom set up of both warp and fill yarns or from more than one warp loom set up, provided that all fibre and fabric properties are uniform and acceptable throughout.

■ **fabric prepreg batch**

prepreg containing one fabric batch impregnated with one batch of resin in one continuous operation.

■ **facade**

the front of a building. Frequently, in architectural terms an artificial or decorative effort.

■ **face**

1. the exposed surface of a wall or masonry unit.
2. the surface of a unit designed to be exposed in the finished masonry.

■ **face-centred cubic**

a crystal structure found in some of the common elemental metals. Within the cubic unit cell, atoms are located at all corner and face-centred positions.

■ **faceshell bedding**

in concrete block masonry construction application of mortar to all vertical and horizontal edges of the face shells of hollow masonry units.

■ **facia or fascia**

a flat board, band, or face, used sometimes by itself but usually in combination with mouldings, often located at the outer face of the cornice.

■ **factory mutual fm**

a major insurance agency who has established stringent guidelines for maximum construction integrity as it relates to fire and environmental hazards. Their specifications have become industry standards.

■ **factory seam**

a splice/seam made by the manufacturer during the assembly of sections of materials into large sheets.

■ **fahrenheit scale**

a thermometric scale on, which the freezing point of water is at 32 degrees above the 0 on the scale, and the boiling point is at 212 degrees.

■ **failure**

1. a state of inability to perform a normal function; a fracturing or giving way under stress.
2. deterioration or decay, especially of qualities such as strength, etc. 'the failure of the roof membrane made its retirement necessary' fan pressurisation. Most buildings rely on some form of ventilation system to exhaust contaminated air. This system may run continuously, or may be operated automatically or manually. Ventilation systems can be of three types: a) exhaust only, resulting in a lower air pressure inside a building relative to the outside and increased infiltration; b) supply only, raising the pressure inside a building and increasing exfiltration, and c) balanced, with both supply and exhaust being operated by fans even in a balanced system, the amount of air may be increased or decreased relative to the amount being exhausted, increasing or decreasing the inside pressure accordingly.

■ **failure rate**

the number of failures of an item per unit measure of life (cycles, time, miles, events, etc., as applicable for the item).

■ **fallback**

a reduction in the softening point temperature of asphalt that occurs when asphalt is heated for pro-longed periods at elevated temperature. (See **softening point drift**.)

■ **fascia**

a vertical or steeply sloped roof or trim located at the perimeter of a building. Typically, it is a border for the low-slope roof system that waterproofs the interior portions of the building.

■ **fascia girder**

the outermost girder on each side of a bridge.

■ **fastener**

a mechanical device, weld or rivet for holding two or more parts together in a structure. Nails and screws are examples of fasteners, which may also be called connectors in certain contexts.

■ **fasteners**

any of a wide variety of mechanical securement devices and assemblies, including nails, screws, cleats, clips, and bolts, which may be used to secure various components of a roof assembly.

■ **fatigue**

the deterioration of a pavement or other structure caused by the action of repetitive vehicle loads.

■ **fatty surface**

designated by areas where the bitumen has bled to the surface. Can become soft in hot weather.

■ **Fe**

Iron.

■ **feasibiltiy structure**

1. analysis of the practicability of a proposal; e.g., a description and analysis of the potential cleanup alternatives for a site on the National Priorities List. The feasibility study usually recommends selection of a cost-effective alternative. It usually starts as soon as the remedial investigation is underway; together, they are commonly referred to as the RI/FS.
2. in research, a small-scale investigation of a problem to ascertain whether or not a proposed research approach is likely to provide useful data.

■ **feathering**

a slowly changing rate of valvespool position between fully open and fully closed in which the fluid is throttled. Term sometimes used synonymously with 'throttling'.

■ **feature carried**

the roadway, railway, or pathway that is carried by the bridge.

■ **feature crossed**

the roadway, railway, ravine, stream, or other physical feature that is crossed over by the bridge.

■ **faecal coliform**

that portion of the coliform bactèria group which is present in the intestinal tracts and faeces of warm-blooded animals.

■ **feed**

the portion of the work cycle in, which work is performed on the workpiece.

■ **feedback**

a signal, which represents the output action of a hydraulic component or function. Also a device, which monitors the action of a hydraulic component or function.

■ **feedback loop**

a control loop in, which the measured variable is fed back and compared with the desired value, and the difference is used as the input to the controller.

■ **felt**

a flexible sheet manufactured by the interlocking of fibres through a combination of mechanical work, moisture, and heat. Roofing felts may be manufactured principally from wood pulp and vegetable fibres (organic felts), asbestos fibres (asbestos felts), glass fibres (fibreglass felts or ply sheet), or polyester fibres.

■ **felt machine (felt layer)**

a mechanical device used for applying bitumen and roofing felt or ply sheet simultaneously.

■ **Fermi energy**

for a metal, the energy corresponding to the highest filled electron state in the valence bond at 0 K.

■ **ferrite (iron)**

body-centered cubic iron. Also, iron and steel alloys that have the BCC crystal structure.

■ **ferroelectric**

a dielectric material that may exhibit polarisation in the absence of an electric field.

■ **ferrography**

a laboratory technique for examining and assessing wear particles entrained in a fluid using a magnetic field.

■ **ferromagnetism**

permanent and large magnetisations found in some metals (e.g., Fe, Ni, and Co), which result from the parallel alignments of neighbouring magnetic moments.

■ **ferrule**

a small metal sleeve placed inside a gutter at the top. A spike is nailed through the gutter into the fascia board to hold the gutter in place. The ferrule acts as a spacer in the gutter to maintain its original shape.

■ **fibre**

any material that has been drawn into a cylinder with a length-to-diameter ratio greater than about ten.

■ **fibreglass insulation**

blanket or rigid board insulation, composed of glass fibres bound together with a binder, faced or unfaced, used to insulate roofs and walls. Rigid boards usually have an asphalt and craft paper facer.

■ **field**

the expanse of wall between openings, corners, etc., principally composed of stretchers.

■ **field capacity**

the capacity of soil to hold water. It is measured by the soil scientist as the ratio of the weight of water retained by the soil to the weight of the dry soil.

■ **field change sheets**

changes to the PS&E package prepared by the designer after project award and prior to construction.

■ **field of the roof**

the central or main portion of a roof, excluding the perimeter and flashing.

■ **field seam**

a splice or seam made in the field (not factory) where overlapping sheets are joined together using an adhesive, splicing tape, or heat- or solvent-welding.

■ **filler**

a fine material, the majority of which passes a 0.075 mm sieve, derived from aggregate or other similar granular material and commonly used in slurry sealing and asphalt.

■ **filler (wood)**

a heavily pigmented preparation used for fining and levelling off the pores in open-pored woods.

■ **filter**

a device used to remove solids from a mixture or to separate materials. Materials are frequently separated from water using filters.

■ **filter block**

a hollow, vitrified clay masonry unit, sometimes salt-glassed, de-signed for trickling filter floors in sewage disposal plants.

■ **filtration**

the mechanical process, which removes particulate matter by separating water from solid material, usually by passing it through sand.

■ **fine aggregate**

a general term for aggregate of such size that it substantially passes a sieve of specified size, commonly 4.75 mm.

■ **fire clay**

a clay which is highly resistant to heat without deforming and used for making brick.

■ **fire point**

the temperature at, which a liquid will burn continuously when ignited by a small flame under carefully specified conditions.

■ **fire resistive material**

non-combustible material.

■ **fire retardant chemical**

a chemical or preparation of chemicals used to reduce flammability or to retard spread of flame.

■ **fire stop**

a solid, tight closure of a concealed space, placed to prevent the spread of fire and smoke through such a space. In a frame wall, this will usually consist of 2 by 4 cross blocking between studs.

■ **fire wall**

any wall built for the purpose of restricting or preventing the spread of fire in a building. Such walls of solid masonry or concrete generally sub-divided a building from the foundations to two or more feet above the plane of the roof.

■ **fireproofing**

any material or combination protecting structural members to increase their fire resistance.

■ **fire-resistive**

in the absence of a specific ruling by the authority having jurisdiction, applies to materials for construction not combustible in the temperatures of ordinary fires and that will withstand such fires without serious impairment of their usefulness for at least 1 hour.

■ **fire-setting**

an ancient tunneling technique in which rock is heated with fire and then doused with cold water, causing the rock to fracture.

■ **firing**

a high-temperature heat treatment that increases the density and strength of a ceramic piece.

■ **fishmouth**

(also referred to as an Edge Wrinkle) 1. a half-cylindrical or half-conical shaped opening or void in a lapped edge or seam, usually caused by wrinkling or shifting of ply sheets during installation; 2. in shingles, a half-conical opening formed at a cut edge.

■ **fishplate**

a wood or plywood piece used to fasten the ends of two members together at a butt joint with nails or bolts. Sometimes used at the junction of opposite rafters near the ridge line.

■ **fixed ground water**

water held in saturated material with pore spaces so small that it is permanently attached to the prewalls, or moves so slowly that it is usually not available as a source of water for pumping.

■ **fixed support**

in terms of bridge bearings, a support that allows rotation only. In analysis, this type of connection is commonly defined as 'pinned'.

■ **flagstone (flagging or flags)**

flat stones, from 1 to 4 inches thick, used for rustic walks, steps, floors, and the like.

■ **flake**

a scale like particle. To lose bond from a surface in small thin pieces. Sometimes a paint film 'flakes'.

■ **flaking**

detachment of a uniform layer of a coating or surface material, usually related to internal movement, lack of adhesion, or passage of moisture.

■ **flange connection**

a block of metal in, which tubing or a conduit is terminated and bolted to the equipment or to a companion flange to form a union connection.

■ **flared wall**

wingwall that is between an in-line wingwall and a U-wingwall.

flash point

the temperature at, which a liquid gives off sufficient flammable vapours to ignite when approached by a small flame under carefully specified conditions.

flashing

1. a thin impervious material placed in the mortar joints and through air spaces in masonry to provide water drainage and prevent water penetration.
2. manufacturing method used to produce specific colour tones.
3. connecting devices that seal membrane joints at expansion joints, walls, drains, gravel stops, and other places where the membrane is interrupted or terminated.

flashing base

the upturned edge of the watertight membrane formed at a roof termination point by the extension of the felts vertically over the cant strip and up the wall for a varying distance where they are secured with mechanical fasteners.

flashing cement

as used by the roofing industry, an ASTM D 2822 Type II roof cement that is a trowelable mixture of solvent-based bitumen and mineral stabilisers that may include asbestos or other inorganic or organic fibres. Generally, flashing cement is characterised as vertical-grade, which indicates it is intended for use on vertical surfaces.

flashing or flashing tape

a thin, impervious material used in construction to prevent water penetration; commonly used to seal contacts around window and door frames.

flashing, counter

the formed metal secured to a wall, curb, or roof top unit to cover and protect the upper edge of a base flashing and its associated fasteners.

flashing, step

individual small pieces of metal flashing material used to flash around chimneys, dormers, and such projections along the slope of a roof. The individual pieces are overlapped and stepped up the vertical surface.

flashing, thru-wall

flashing extended completely through a masonry wall. Designed and applied in combination with counter flashings, to prevent water which may enter the wall above from proceeding downward in the wall or into the roof deck or roofing system.

flat paint

an interior paint that contains a high proportion of pigment and dries to a flat or lustreless finish.

flat seam

a seam at the junction of sheet metal roof components that has been bent at the plane of the roof.

flexible pavement

a pavement which obtains its load spreading properties mainly by inter granular pressure, mechanical interlock and cohesion between the particles of the pavement material. In the case of an asphalt pavement, this further depends on the adhesions between the bitumen binder and the aggregate, and the cohesion of the binder. Generally, any pavement in which high strength portland cement concrete is not used a construction layer.

■ flood

a flood is an overflow or inundation that comes from a river or other body of water and causes or threatens damage. It can be any relatively high streamflow overtopping the natural or artificial banks in any reach of a stream. It is also a relatively high flow as measured by either gauge height or discharge quantity.

■ flood (pour) coat

the surfacing layer of bitumen into which surfacing aggregate is embedded on an aggregate surfaced built-up roof. A flood coat is generally thicker and heavier than a glaze coat, and is applied at approximately 45-60 pounds per square (2-3 kilograms per meter).

■ flood plain

a strip of relatively level land bordering a stream or river. It is built of sediment carried by the stream and dropped when the water has flooded the area. It is called a water flood plain if it is overflowed in times of highwater, or a fossil flood plain if it is beyond the reach of the highest flood.

■ flooded suction

refers to a pump suction port, which is pressurised by a natural gravitational or elevated head of fluid (reservoir oil level is above the pump inlet port) or flooded by a charging or booster pump.

■ floodway

1. a part of the flood plain. The channel of a river or stream; the parts of the flood plains adjoining the channel, which are reasonably required to carry and discharge the flood water or floodflow of any river or stream.
2. the area along both sides of a bayou or creek including the main channel that has the strictest regulations on it because it is the area that is needed to move the 1% flood downstream and out of the homes or businesses that it may have flooded.

■ floor beam

a transverse primary member in a truss or girder system that runs between the longitudinal primary members.

■ flop

cutting of felts into strips, coating the deck side with bitumen and placing (flopping) the felt onto the deck.

■ flow

the movement of a volume of fluid in a hydraulic passage produced by a pressure differential.

■ **flow control**

a device, which regulates the rate of fluid flow.

■ **flow fatigue**

the ability of a component to resist structural failure due to flexing caused by A differential pressure created by a variable flow rate.

■ **flow forces**

the forces arising from high fluid velocity, particularly at spool lands,, which manifest themselves in undesirable induced forces.

■ **flow gain**

the slope of the control flow vs. input signal curve in any specific operating region, under specific conditions.

■ **flow lock**

the impediment of the actuating member of a valve caused by induced axial thrust due to the change in fluid momentum.

■ **flow metering characteristics**

a family of output flow versus input signal curves.

■ **flow rate**

the volume, mass, or weight of fluid passing through a flow passage per unit time.

■ **flow, compressibility**

a flow resulting from a change in pressure.

■ **flow, couette**

flow that occurs as a result of relative velocity between fluid and mechanical element.

■ **flow, deformation**

a flow due to the distortion of the enclosure material.

■ **flow, displacement**

a flow due to the variation of the piston displacement.

■ **flow, interstitial**

this flow occurs due to the differential pressure across a seal contact area and within the interstices, which are bounded by the asperities of the topography and the fluid film.

■ **flow, laminar**

a condition of a moving fluid stream exhibiting streamlines in, which the Reynolds number is less than 2000.

■ **flow, poiseulle**

flow that occurs as a result of a pressure gradient.

■ **flow, pulsation frequency**

this is the number of flow ripples that occur during a unit time period.

■ **flow, pulsation magnitude ratio**

this ratio is the difference between the maximum flow and the minimum flow to the mean flow, expressed as a percent.

■ **flow, steady state**

a flow situation in, which conditions such as pressure, temperature, and velocity at any point in the fluid do not change with time.

■ **flow, transition**

the flow pattern that occurs between laminar and turbulent flow regimes.

■ **flow, turbulent**

a condition of a moving fluid exhibiting random flow vectors and a Reynolds number greater than 4000.

■ **flow, unsteady**

a flow condition in, which quantities such as pressure, velocity and temperature change with time at some fixed point in the fluid.

■ **flowing wells**

a well where the piezometric surface lies above the ground surface.

■ **flue**

the space or passage in a chimney through which smoke, gas, or fumes ascend. Each passage is called a flue, which together with any others and the surrounding masonry make up the chimney.

■ **flue lining**

fire clay or terra-cotta pipe, round or square, usually made in all ordinary flue sizes and in 2-foot lengths, used for the inner lining of chimneys with the brick or masonry work around the outside. Flue lining in chimneys runs from about a foot below the flue connection to the top of the chimney.

■ **fluid**

a substance (either liquid or gas), which yields to any pressure tending to alter its shape. The state of matter that is not solid and is able to flow and change shape.

■ **fluid conditioner**

a device, which is used to control the physical characteristics of a fluid.

■ **fluid oxidation**

a chemical breakdown of a fluid, causing the formation of oxidation products,, which in turn cause emulsification, foaming, and the deposition of varnishes and sludge.

■ **fluid power**

power transmitted and controlled through use of a pressurised fluid (liquid or gas).

■ **fluid velocity**

the linear speed at, which fluid is flowing past a specific point in a hydraulic circuit.

■ **fluid, fire-resistant**

a fluid not easily ignited.

■ **fluid, flash point**

the temperature at, which a fluid first gives off sufficient flammable vapour to ignite when approached by a small flame or spark.

■ **fluid, hydraulic**

a liquid that is specially compounded for use as a power-transmitting medium in a hydraulic system.

■ **fluid, non-flammable**

a fluid that cannot be ignited.

■ **fluid, pour point**

the lowest temperature of a fluid at, which it will flow or can be poured.

■ **fluid, stability**

resistance of a fluid to permanent change in properties chemical, thermal, mechanical and contamination.

■ **fluid, viscosity**

a measure of the internal friction or the resistance of fluid to flow.

■ **fluid-applied elastomer**

a liquid elastomeric material that cures after application to form a continuous waterproofing membrane.

■ **fluidity**

the inverse of viscosity and expresses the flow properties of a fluid.

■ **flushed seal**

a seal in which the bitumen has bled to the surface.

■ **flux**

a liquid, normally diesel or oil, added to bitumen to give a long term reduction in viscosity.

■ **fly rafters**

end rafters of the gable overhang supported by roof sheathing and lookouts.

■ **flyash**

the ash residue from high temperature combustion processes. Electric power plants using western coal, such as Austin's Fayette plant, produce a non—toxic flyash that can be a substitute for cement. Municipal waster incinerators can produce a toxic flyash, which is not recommended as a component of any building material.

■ **FMECA**

'Failure Mode, Effects and Criticality Analysis' is a procedure designed to document all conceivable potential failures of a system or component, the effect of each failure on system operation, and identify those that are critical to operational success and personnel safety.

■ **foam**

an intimate mixture of air and liquid occupying much more volume than the liquid alone. It is generally caused by the release of air in solution caused by reducing the pressure and is most prevalent in the reservoir.

■ **foamed bitumen**

hot bitumen greatly expanded in volume by the introduction of steam and water. Can be used for spray sealing in situ stabilisation (foam stab) and for production of foam mixed aggregate products (foamix).

■ **fog**

a cloud of condensed water vapour near the ground.

■ **fog seal**

refer enrichment seal.

■ **folded seam**

in sheet metal work, a joint between sheets of metal wherein the edges of the sheets are crimped together and folded flat.

■ **footing**

the base of a substructure that transfers the load from the structure to the soil, rock, or from the structure to the piles.

■ **forbay**

the water behind a dam.

■ **force**

the total tendency to assist or oppose the movement of an object, it is a push or pull measured in units of weight. In hydraulics, force is expressed by the product of pressure and the area of the surface on, which the pressure acts.

■ **forging**

mechanical forming of a metal or alloy by heating and hammering.

■ **forging dies**

a piece of precision-made mass production tooling used by industrial blacksmiths to drop or hammer forge engine crankshafts, axles, engine connecting rods, turbine blades, steering arms, and small hand tools such as spanners, axe heads, hammer heads, and shear blades.

■ **form**

a temporary structure that acts as a mould for concrete until it has cured enough to support itself.

■ **form liner**

a mould attached to the inside face of a form to introduce an aesthetic surface effect on the exposed face of the concrete.

■ **formaldehyde**

a colourless, pungent smelling material used as an adhering component of glues in many wood products. It can cause respiratory problems, cancer and chemical sensitivity.

■ **formaldehyde off gas**

APA trademarked structural wood panels, such as plywood and oriented strand board, are made with phenol formaldehyde adhesives, which should not be confused with urea formaldehyde adhesives. Formaldehyde-related problems have been associated with certain urea formaldehyde adhesives but not with the phenol formaldehyde adhesives. In fact, because formaldehyde levels associated with phenolic resin-bonded products are so low, these products are exempted from the department of housing and urban development testing and certification requirements.

■ **formwork**

the entire system of forms for a structure.

■ **foundation**

the lower supporting part of an engineering structure in contact with the underlying soil or rock and transmitting the weight of the structure and its included loads to the underlying earth material.

■ **four-way valve**

a valve having four distinct and separate flow paths.

■ **fracture critical**

a tension member whose failure due to fracture would lead to the collapse of the structure.

■ **fracture toughness**

critical value of the stress intensity factor for which crack extensions occurs.

■ **framing**

a system of structural elements, woodwork or rough timber of a building structure, such as partitions, flooring and roofing, or any framed work as around an opening in an exterior wall.

■ **framing plan**

a detail drawing that shows the length, spacing, types, and azimuths of the girders and cross frames.

■ **framing, balloon**

a system of framing a building in which all vertical structural elements of the bearing walls and partitions consist of single pieces extending from the top of the foundation sin plate to the roof plate and to which all floor joists are fastened.

■ **framing, platform**

a system of framing a building in which floor joists of each story rest on the top plates of the story below or on the foundation sill for the first story, and the bearing walls and partitions rest on the sub floor of each story.

■ **free energy**

a thermodynamic quantity that is a function of both the internal energy and entropy of a system.

■ **free ground water**

water in interconnected pore spaces in the zone of saturation down to the first impervious barrier, moving under the control of the water table slope.

■ **freezing**

the change of a liquid into a solid as temperature decreases. For water, the freezing point is 32 °F or 0 °C.

■ **frenkel defect**

in an ionic solid, a cation-vacancy and cation-interstitial pair.

■ **frequency response**

the performance of a system at various frequencies of sinusoidal input signal. The ratio of output to input magnitude is plotted against the input frequency. In a servovalve, frequency response is normally measured with constant input current amplitude and zero load pressure drop, expressed as amplitude ratio, and phase angle.

■ **fresh salt water interface**

the region where fresh water and salt water meet.

■ **fretting**

surface destruction caused by vibration existing between two surfaces in intimate contact with each and having an oscillatory relative motion of small amplitude.

■ **friction**

the resistance to motion of an object under the action of an external force. Fluid friction is the internal friction of a liquid and better known as viscosity.

■ **friction course**

a specialised wearing course constructed of open graded asphalt.

■ **friction losses**

the pressure energy losses due to friction stem from Darcy's formula and the modified Moody diagram for friction factor.

■ **friction pile**

a pile whose primary support comes from friction between the pile and the soil.

■ **frieze**

in house construction a horizontal member connecting the top of the siding with the soffit of the cornice.

■ **frog**

a depression in the bed surface of a brick. Sometimes called a panel.

■ **frost**

a covering of minute ice crystals on a cold surface. The temperature that causes freezing (32 degrees Fahrenheits or below).

■ **frostline**

the depth of frost penetration in soil. This depth varies in different parts of the country. Footings should be placed below this depth to prevent movement.

■ **FSIP forms**

Foam-filled Stay-In-Place Forms. SIP Forms that have a foam insert in the corrugations to replace some of the concrete and reduce the dead load. See also, **SIP forms.**

■ **full depth asphalt pavement**

a pavement in which asphalt is used for all courses above the sub grade or improved sub grade.

■ **full flow**

a condition where all the fluid must pass through the component or medium.

■ **fully adhered**

a completely attached (adhered) roof membrane.

■ **function**

a characteristic behaviour given by an expression such that for each value of x within a range there is an associated value, or several values, of the variable y. Therefore y is a function of x.

■ **fungi, wood**

microscopic plants that live in damp wood and cause mould, stain, and decay.

■ **fungicide**

a chemical that is poisonous to fungi.

■ **furring**

method of finishing the interior face of a concrete or masonry wall: it consist of wood strips which provide space for insulation, allow space for measures to prevent moisture transmittance, and provide a flat, level substrate for finishing. Strips of wood or metal applied to a wall or other surface to even it and normally to serve as a fastening base for finish material.

■ **fuzzy logic**

the logic of approximating reasoning using possibility functions.

■ **gabion**

wire mesh baskets filled with rocks and stacked on top of one another to serve as a retaining wall.

■ **gable**

a triangular portion of the endwall of a building directly under the sloping roof and above the eave line.

■ **gable**

the end of a building as distinguished from the front or rear side. The triangular end of and exterior wall from the level of the eaves to the ridge of a double sloped roof.

■ **gable**

in house construction, the portion of the roof above the eave line of a double-sloped roof.

■ **gable end**

an end wall having a gable.

■ **gable-end roof**

a roof that slopes upward on two sides. See **diagram**.

■ **gable-shaped roof**

a single-ridge roof that terminates at gable end(s).

■ **gauge**

1. generic term for measuring instruments.
2. a measure of the fineness of knitted fabrics expressing the number of needles per unit of width.

■ **gauge length**

length over which deformation is measured. The original length of that portion of the specimen over which strain or change of length is determined.

■ **gauge length, effective**

in tensile testing, it is the estimated length of the specimen subjected to a strain equal to that observed for the true length.

■ **gauge length, nominal**

in tensile testing, it is the length of a specimen under pre-tension measured from nip-to-nip of the jaws of the holding clamp in their starting position.

■ **gauging station**

the site on a stream, lake or canal where hydrologic data is collected.

■ **gain**

the ratio of output magnitude to input magnitude.

■ **gain margin**

the amount of control loop gain in decibels that can be increased before the system reaches instability.

■ **galling**

an adhesion condition, which arises from a combination of materials, which possess either poor bearing characteristics or are operated with improper or no lubrication. This wear mechanism results in the transfer of material from one member to the other member in such a manner as to cause extremely high force to move the members relative to each other. Galling can result in both members virtually locked together.

■ **gallon**

a unit of volume. A U.S. gallon contains 231 cu. in., 0.133 cubic feet, or 3.785 liters. One U.S. gallon of water weighs 8.3 lbs.

■ **galvanise**

to coat a metal with zinc by dipping in molten zinc after cleaning.

■ **gambrel roof**

a type of roof which has its slope broken by an obtuse angle, so that the lower slope is steeper than the upper slope. A double sloped roof having two pitches.

■ **gap graded aggregate**

a graded aggregate in which one or more of the intermediate sizes are absent

■ **gas**

a state of matter; a substance that generally exists in the gaseous phase at room temperature.

■ **gasket**

a device, which is used between two relatively static surfaces to prevent leakage and is made of several deformable materials.

■ **gauge**

the thickness of sheet metal and wire, etc.

■ **gauge pressure**

pressure of a system over and above atmospheric pressure. The difference between absolute pressure and atmospheric pressure. It is the pressure used to calculate the forces exerted in a hydraulic system.

■ **generated contaminant**

It is contaminant produced due to the deterioration of surfaces, various tribological wear mechanisms, incompatible materials, etc. A product of system activity and inactivity

■ **generator**

a machine that changes water power, steam power, or other

kinds of mechanical energy into electricity.

geographic information system (GIS)

a computer program used to store different types of information and link that information to a specific location. Some examples of this information would be streets, bayous and channels, HCAD parcel data, contours, floodplains and all the data that supports this information such as names, location and much more.

geohydrology

a term, which denotes the branch of hydrology relating to subsurface or subterranean waters; that is, to all waters below the surface.

geologic erosion

normal or natural erosion caused by geological processes acting over long geologic periods and resulting in the wearing away of mountains, the building up of flood plains, coastal plains, etc.

geology

the science dealing with the general study of the earth.

geomorphology

the study of the classification, description, nature, origin and development of present landforms and their relationship to underlying structures.

geopressured reservoir

a geothermal reservoir consisting of porous sands containing water or brine at high temperature or pressure.

geotechnics

the application of scientific methods and engineering principles to the acquisition, interpretation and use of knowledge of materials of the Earth's crust for the solution of engineering problems

geothermal energy

the heat energy available in the earth's subsurface, extracted from three basic sources; 1. steam; 2. hot water; and 3. hot rocks or near surface intrusions of volcanic molten rock. The normal thermal gradient of the earth's crust is such that the temperature in a deep well or mine increased by about 1 °F for each 100 feet of depth.

geyser

a periodic thermal spring that results from the expansive force of super heated steam.

girder

a large or principal beam of wood or steel used to support concentrated loads at isolated points along its length.

glacier

a huge mass of land ice that consists of recrystallised snow and moves slowly downslope or outward.

■ **gland**

the cavity of a stuffing box.

■ **glass**

an inorganic product of fusion which has cooled to a rigid condition without crystallising.

■ **glass felt**

a sheet composed of bonded glass fibres, suitable for impregnation and coating in the manufacture of bituminous roofing and waterproofing materials, and shingles.

■ **glass mat**

a thin mat composed of glass fibres, woven or non-woven, with or without a binder. This mat may serve as reinforcement for certain roof materials and membranes.

■ **glass-ceramic**

a fine-grained crystalline material that was formed as a glass and subsequently devitrified (crystallised).

■ **glaze coat**

1. the top layer of asphalt on a smooth-surfaced built-up roof membrane.
2. a thin protective coating of bitumen applied to the lower plies or top ply of a built-up roof membrane when application of additional felts or the flood coat and aggregate surfacing are delayed. (Also see **flood coat**.)

■ **global positioning system**

a system, which verifies latitude and longitude of a location on the ground through the use of a transmitter and a remote (satellite) vehicle.

■ **global positioning system (GPS)**

GPS is a system that uses satellites to accurately determine the location of any point on earth, and it helps to create the most accurate floodplain maps possible.

■ **gloss (paint or enamel)**

a paint or enamel that contains a relatively low proportion of pigment and dries to a sheen or lustre.

■ **gloss enamel**

a finishing material made of varnish and sufficient pigments to provide opacity and colour, but little or no pigment of low opacity. Such an enamel forms a hard coating with maximum smoothness of surface and a high degree of gloss.

■ **glue laminated**

a large timber member formed by gluing layers of smaller timber members together.

■ **grading aggregate**

the quantities of the various particle sizes present in a mineral aggregate, expressed as a percentage by mass of the whole. Also referred to as particle size distribution.

■ **grain, edge (vertical)**

edge-grain lumber has been sawed parallel to the pith of the log and approximately at right angles to the growth rings; i.e., the rings form an angle of 45° or more with the surface of the piece.

■ **grain, flat**

flat-grain lumber has been sawed parallel to the pith of the log and approximately tangent to the growth rings, i.e., the rings form an angle of less than 45° with the surface of the piece.

■ **grain, quartersawn**

another term for edge grain.

■ **granite**

granites are dense and hard rocks that resist wear and often have a speckled appearance. While geologically the term 'granite' is really restricted to certain crystalline rocks of igneous origin made up of quartz, feldspar and mica, in the stone and masonry industry the term is used for almost all igneous rocks with an interlocking granular texture. For example, black granite refers to black, fine-grained igneous rocks such as basalt and dia base, which scientifically speaking are not granite. Granites have low porosity and permeability, which gives most of them a high resistance to weathering, although some may be susceptible to iron staining. Granite is often used in construction and landscaping components that are in contact with the ground (steps, walkways, even foundations) in predominantly brick, limestone or sandstone buildings.

■ **granular pavement**

refer flexible pavement.

■ **granule**

(also referred to as Mineral or Ceramic Granule) opaque, natural, or synthetically coloured aggregate commonly used to surface cap sheets, shingles, and other granule-surfaced roof coverings.

■ **grassed waterway**

a natural or constructed waterway, usually broad and shallow and covered with erosion-resistant grasses, used to conduct surface water from cropland.

■ **gravel**

loose fragments of rock used for surfacing built-up roofs, in sizes varying from 1/8 inches to 1 3/4 inches.

■ **gravel stop**

a low profile upward-projecting metal edge flashing with a flange along the roof side, usually formed from sheet or extruded metal. Installed along the perimeter of a roof to provide a continuous finished edge for roofing material. Acts as a bitumen-stop during mop application of hot bitumen along a perimeter edge.

■ **gravity dam**

a dam constructed so that its great weight resists the force of water pressure.

■ **graywater**

water that has been used for showering, clothes washing, and faucet uses. Kitchen sink and toilet water is excluded. This water has excellent potential to be reused as irrigation for yards.

■ **grit**

small size aggregate 5 mm or less.

■ **ground water**

the supply of fresh water found beneath the Earth's surface (usually in aquifers), which is often used for supplying wells and springs. Because ground water is a major source of drinking water, there is growing concern over areas where leaching agricultural or industrial pollutants or substances from leaking underground storage tanks are contaminating ground water.

■ **ground water hydrology**

the branch of hydrology that deals with ground water; its occurrence and movements, its replenishment and depletion, the properties of rocks that control ground water movement and storage, and the methods of investigation and utilization of ground water.

■ **ground water recharge**

the inflow to a ground water reservoir.

■ **ground water reservoir**

an aquifer or aquifer system in, which ground water is stored. The water may be placed in the aquifer by artificial or natural means.

■ **ground water runoff**

a portion of runoff, which has passed into the ground, has become ground water, and has been discharged into a stream channel as spring or seepage water.

■ **ground water storage**

the storage of water in ground water reservoirs.

■ **grounds**

guides used around openings and at the floor line to strike off plaster. They can consist of narrow strips of wood or of wide subjambs at interior doorways. They provide a level plaster line for installation of casing and other trim.

■ **grout**

a thin mixture of cementitious material and aggregate to which sufficient water is added to produce pouring consistency without segregation of the constituents. High-lift grouting: the technique of grouting masonry in lifts up to 12 ft. Low-lift grouting: the technique of grouting as the wall is constructed.

■ **grout or grouting**

a cement mortar mixture commonly used to fill joints and cavities of masonry. On roof decks, the joints between many types of pre-cast roof deck slabs are grouted with cement grout.

■ **gully**

a deeply eroded channel caused by the concentrated flow of water.

■ **gully erosion**

the development of relatively deep, steep-sided channels from small rills and water courses that have not been eradicated with tillage and have become too deep to permit normal farming operations.

■ **gum**

a rubber-like, sticky deposit, black or dark brown in colour,, which results from oxidation of lubricating oil.

■ **gusset**

a flat wood, plywood, or similar type member used to provide a connection at intersection of wood members. Most commonly used at joints of wood trusses. They are fastened by nails, screws, bolts, or adhesives.

■ **gusset plate**

steel plate used to connect steel members together.

■ **gutter**

a channelled component installed along the downslope perimeter of a roof to convey runoff water from the roof to the drain leaders or downspouts.

■ **gutter or nave trough**

a shallow channel or conduit of metal or wood set below and along the eaves of a house to catch and carry off rainwater from the roof.

■ **gutter strap**

metal bands used to support the gutter.

■ **guy wire**

a strong steel wire or cable strung from an anchor on the roof to any tall slender projection for the purpose of support.

■ **gypsum**

a hydrated sulphate of calcium occurring naturally in sedimentary rock. In roofing, a type of lightweight deck made from this pulverised rock.

■ **gypsum plaster**

gypsum formulated to be used with the addition of sand and water for base-coat plaster.

■ **gypsum/cellulose**

an interior wallboard product that uses cellulose from recycled newspapers with gypsum and perlite.

■ **h_{50} value**

a drop height with a 50% probability of reaction, as determined experimentally by the Bruceton up-and-down method.

■ **hackle**

a structured fracture surface marking giving a matte or roughened appearance to the surface and possessing varying degrees of coarseness.

■ **hackle marks**

fine ridges on a fracture surface, parallel to the direction of propagation of the fracture.

■ **hail**

a form of precipitation, which forms into balls or lumps of ice over 0.2 inch in diameter. Hail is formed by alternate freezing and melting as it is carried up and down in highly turbulent air currents.

■ **Half-hard**

referring to the temper of nonferrous alloys and some ferrous alloys which have tensile strength about midway between dead-soft and full-hard tempers.

■ **Hall effect**

the phenomenon- whereby a force is brought to bear on a moving electron or hole by a magnetic field that is applied perpendicular to the direction of motion. The force direction is perpendicular to both the magnetic field and the particle motion directions.

■ **hardenability**

a measure of the depth to which a specific ferrous alloy may be hardened by the formation of martensite upon quenching from a temperature above the upper critical temperature.

■ **hardness**

the measure of some materials' resistance to deformation by surface indentation or by abrasion.

■ **hardpan**

a shallow layer of earth material, which has become relatively hard and impermeable, usually through the deposition of minerals.

■ **harsh**

refers to an asphalt mix that is difficult to compact and handle.

■ **harvested rainwater**

the rain that falls on a roof or yard and is channelled by gutters or channels to a storage tank. the first wash of water on a roof is usually discarded and the subsequent rainfall is captured for use if the system is being used for potable water. Good quality water is available by this method in most areas.

■ **hatch**

an opening in a deck; floor or roof. The usual purpose is to provide access from inside the building.

■ **haunch**

a thickness of concrete below the structural deck and above the top of the girder that is used to accommodate any fabrication or construction tolerances.

■ **haunched girder**

a girder that has a varying web depth along its length.

■ **head**.

the height of a column or body of fluid above a given point expressed in linear units. Pressure is equal to the height times the density of the fluid.

■ **head, pressure**

the vertical distance between a point in a system and the surface of the fluid referenced to the atmosphere.

■ **head-cylinder**

the cylinder end closure, which covers the differential area between the bore area and the piston rod area.

■ **header**

a beam placed perpendicular to joists and to which joists are nailed in framing for chimney, stairway, or other opening. A wood lintel.

■ **headgate**

the gate that controls water flow into irrigation canals and ditches. A watermaster regulates the headgates during water distribution and posts headgate notices declaring official regulations.

■ **headlap**

the distance of overlap measured from the uppermost ply or course to the point that it laps over the undermost ply or course.

■ **health assessment**

an evaluation of data and information gathered on the release of hazardous substances into the environment to assess any current or future impact on public health.

■ **healthy home**

a 'healthy home' is built with least-toxic building materials and is designed to support and contribute to a better indoor environment.

■ **hearth**

the inner or outer floor of a fireplace, usually made of brick, tile, or stone.

■ **heartwood**

the wood extending from the pith to the sapwood, the cells of which no longer participate in the life processes of the tree.

■ **heat**

the form of energy that has the capacity to create warmth or to increase the temperature of a substance. Any energy that is wasted or used to overcome friction is converted to heat. It is measured in calories or British Thermal Units (BTU's). One BTU is the amount of heat required to raise the temperature of one pound of water one degree Fahrenheit.

■ **heat exchanger**

a device, which transfers heat through a conducting wall from one fluid to another.

■ **heat transfer**

the transmission of thermal energy from a location of higher temperature to a location of lower temperature. This can occur by conduction, convection, or radiation.

■ **heat welding**

method of melting and fusing together the overlapping edges of separate sheets or sections of polymer modified bitumen, thermoplastics or some uncured thermoset roofing membranes by the application of heat (in the form of hot air or open flame) and pressure.

■ **heavy duty pavement**

pavement designed for heavy traffic volumes and heavy loads.

■ **heavy metals**

metallic elements with high atomic weights, e.g., mercury, chromium, cadmium, arsenic, and lead. They can damage living things at low concentrations and tend to accumulate in the food chain.

■ **heavy water**

water composed of isotopes of hydrogen of atomic weight greater than 1 or of oxygen greater than 16, or both; especially water composed of ordinary oxygen and the isotope of hydrogen of atomic weight 2; deuterium oxide (D_2O).

■ **heavy water moderated reactor**

a reactor that uses heavy water as its moderator. Heavy water is an excellent moderator and thus permits the use of inexpensive (unenriched) uranium as a fuel.

■ **hexagonal close-packed (HCP)**

a crystal structure found for some metals. The HCP unit cell is of hexagonal geometry and is generated by the stacking of close-packed planes of atoms.

■ **high quality duct system**

this method of designing and installing ductwork avoids potentially significant heating and cooling losses and potential health hazards caused by depressurising or pressurising a house. Manuals J and D calculations are used to engineer the system. All ducts are sealed using a fibrated latex mastic and fibreglass tape, or metal tape meeting SMACNA standard 181. Both inner and outer linings of the duct are sealed. The air handler, support platform, and return plenum are sealed air tight at all joints. Duct tape is not used in any part of the system. The system can be performance tested to ensure proper installation.

■ **highest and best use**

the classification of water based on an analysis of the greatest needs of the future. Certain quantities are reserved for appropriation according to the classification.

■ **hip**

the external angle formed by the meeting of two sloping sides of a roof.

■ **hip roof**

a roof that slopes upward from all four sides of a building requiring a hip rafter at each corner. See diagram.

■ **holding pond**

a small basin or pond designed to hold sediment laden or contaminated water until it can be treated to meet water quality standards or be used in some other way.

hole

for semi-conductors and insulators, a vacant electron state in the valence band that behaves as a positive charge carrier in an electric field.

holiday

an area where a liquid-applied material is missing or absent.

homopolymer

a polymer having a chain structure in which all mer units are of the same type.

horsepower

a standard unit of power or work. One Hp is equal to 550 ft lb. of energy or work done per second, 33,000 ft lb. of work per minute, 0.746 kW, or 42.4 BTU per minute.

hose

a flexible conduit for conveying fluid between components, which may have relative motion. Consists of synthetic elastomer IC tubes reinforced with woven wire or fabric braid or spiral wrapped wire to provide strength and fitted with various types of connectors.

hot mix

refer **asphalt**.

hot rock reservoir

a potential source of geothermal power. The hot rock system requires drilling deep enough to reach heated rock, then fracturing it to create a reservoir into, which water can be pumped. This technique has not yet been perfected.

hot working

any metal forming operation that is performed above a metal recrystallisation temperature.

h-piles

rolled steel shapes that are proportioned so that they can be used as substructure piles.

humid

containing or characterised by perceptible moisture. Usually refers to the atmosphere.

humidifier

a device designed to increase the humidity within a room or a house by means of the discharge of water vapour. They may consist of individual room size units or larger units attached to the heating plant to condition the entire house.

humidity

the amount of moisture contained in the atmosphere. Generally expressed as percent relative humidity (the ratio of the amount of moisture [water vapour] actually present in the air, compared to the maxi-mum amount that the air could contain at the same temperature.)

hunting

a low frequency instability in, which the output of a unit or system moves back and forth without command input. The action of an improperly damped or unstable system in, which the actuator moves alternately to both sides of a required position before coming to rest, if at all. Sometimes caused by looseness in the input system.

■ **hurricane strap or clip**

a mechanical device used to anchor and attach various elements of a structure to other elements, such as attaching roofing rafters to wall framing or wall framing to foundations. Straps and clips are designed to reduce the likelihood of movement between structural elements.

■ **hvac**

heating, ventilating, and air conditioning equipment.

■ **hydraulic balance**

a condition of equal opposed hydraulic forces acting on an element in a hydraulic component. That is, a condition in, which opposing hydraulic forces are equal.

■ **hydraulic detent**

a valve configuration, which applies the open actuator port pressure against an axial control surface of the spool to hold the valve spool position until a greater axial force is applied to shift the valve in the opposite direction.

■ **hydraulic fuse**

a hydraulic fuse is designed to provide excess flow protection. It automatically shuts off any line in, which failure (component rupture or fracture) has occurred and where hydraulic fluid spews out of a system. It is analogous to an electrical safety device called a "fuse" in, which a strip of metal melts and interrupts the circuit when the current exceeds a particular amperage. These devices consist of various types of excess-flow valves. Such devices are used to block flow and not to relieve pressure as performed by a hydraulic system protector.

■ **hydraulic horsepower**

horsepower computed from the product of flow rate and pressure differential in terms of work performed by the fluid.

■ **hydraulic lock**

a situation in, which a quantity of trapped fluid prevents movement of a piston or other part.

■ **hydraulic motor**

a rotary actuator, which converts pressure energy into rotary energy.

■ **hydraulic null**

the hydraulic neutral or no flow zone of, for example, a four-way servovalve.

■ **hydraulic ram**

a device, which uses the energy of falling water to force a small portion of the water to a height greater than the source.

■ **hydraulic set cement**

a cement that sets through reaction with water.

■ **hydraulics**

if energy transfer is in the form of pressurised liquid flow then it is called hydraulics. The oil is kept in a reservoir and the pump draws it in and pushes it into the system. Because the oils can't escape, pressure builds up and the energy stored in the oil is then used to operate machinery, using high pressure hoses, valves and actuators.

■ **hydro**

the prefix denoting water or hydrogen.

■ **hydrocarbons**

chemical compounds that consist entirely of carbon and hydrogen such as petroleum, natural gas, and coal.

■ **hydrodynamic lubrication**

a condition in, which the shape and relative motion of the sliding surfaces cause the formation of a fluid film having sufficient pressure to separate the two surfaces.

■ **hydrodynamics**

the engineering science dealing with the motion of a fluid and its interactions with its boundaries. For example a jet pump.

■ **hydroelectric**

having to do with production of electricity by water power from falling water.

■ **hydroelectric plant, conventional**

a hydroelectric power plant, which utilises stream flow only once as the water passes downstream, as opposed to a pumped storage plant, which recirculates all or a portion of the stream flow in the production of power.

■ **hydroelectricity**

electric energy production by water powered turbine generators.

■ **hydrogen**

a chemical substance found in most fuels; by itself, a colourless gas that burns quickly. It is a major component of water.

■ **hydrogen bond**

a strong secondary interatomic bond which exists between a bound hydrogen atom (its unscreened proton) and the electrons of adjacent atoms.

■ **hydrogeology**

the science dealing with the occurrence, distribution, and movement of water below the surface of the earth, with a greater emphasis on geology.

■ **hydrograph**

a graphic plot of changes in the flow of water or in the elevation of water level plotted against time.

■ **hydrokinetics**

the engineering science pertaining to the forces produced by a liquid as a result of its motion. For example a centrifugal pump.

■ **hydrologic cycle (water cycle)**

the cycle of water movement from the atmosphere to the earth and back to the atmosphere through various processes. These processes include precipitation, infiltration, percolation, storage, evaporation, transpiration and condensation.

■ **hydrology**

the science dealing with global water (both liquid and solid), its properties, circulation and distribution on or under the Earth's surface and in the atmosphere from the moment of precipitation until it is returned to the atmosphere or discharged into the ocean

■ **hydrolytic stability**

the resistance to permanent changes in properties caused by chemical reaction with water.

■ **hydrometre**

an instrument used to measure the density of a liquid.

■ **hydropower**

power produce by falling water.

■ **hydroseeding**

dissemination of seed under pressure, in a water medium. Mulch, lime, and fertiliser can be incorporated in the spraying mixture.

■ **hydrostatic transmission**

a drive system, which transmits power from a rotary input to a remote rotary output by means of fluid under pressure.

■ **hydrostatics**

the engineering science that deals with the properties of liquids at rest that is, with liquid pressure (in a closed system).

■ **hydrothermal reservoir**

one of three forms of geothermal reservoir systems. It consists of naturally circulating hot water or steam (wet steam) or that which contains mostly vapour (dry steam). The latter type of reservoir is the most desirable type according to present technology.

■ **hygrometre**

an instrument used to measure humidity.

■ **hygroscopic**

a substance, which has a strong affinity for water.

■ **hygroscopic water**

water, which is absorbed from the air.

■ **hypereutectoid alloy**

for an alloy system displaying a eutectoid, an alloy for which the concentration of solute is greater than the eutectoid composition.

■ **hypoeutectoid alloy**

for an alloy system displaying a eutectoid, an alloy for which the concentration of solute is less than the eutectoid composition

■ **hysteresis**

the difference in output value for the same input when this condition is approached from opposite directions. That is, it is the failure to follow the same path in the forward direction as in the backward direction.

■ **hysteresis (magnetic)**

the irreversible magnetic flux density-versus-magnetic field strength (B-versus-H) behaviour found for ferromagnetic and ferrimagnetic materials.

■ **I-beam**

a steel beam with a cross section resembling the letter I. It is used for long spans as basement beams or over wide wall openings, such as a double garage door, when wall and roof loads are imposed on the opening.

■ **ice**

a solid form of water.

■ **ice dam**

a mass of ice formed at the transition from a warm to a cold roof surface, frequently formed by refreezing melt-water at the overhang of a steep roof, causing ice and water to back up under roofing materials.

■ **iceberg**

a large piece of ice that breaks off and floats away from a glacier.

■ **IDF**

abbreviation for Insertion And Deletion Of Fibres.

■ **IGA**

abbreviation for Intergranular Attack.

■ **ignition**

initiation of combustion.

■ **ignition loss**

the difference in weight before and after burning, e.g., as caused by the loss of binder or size.

■ **impact**

a factor used to describe the increase in live load due to the dynamic effect of a vehicle as it moves across a bridge, a.k.a. dynamic load allowance.

■ **impact energy**

a measure of the energy absorbed during the fracture of a specimen of standard dimensions and geometry when subjected to very rapid (impact) loading. Charpy and Izod impact tests are used to measure this parameter, which is important in assessing the ductile-to-brittle transition behaviour of a material.

■ **impact extrusion die**

a piece of precision-made mass production tooling used to impact extrude aluminium drink cans, and steel engine valves, axles, builders' nails and high tensile steel bolts.

■ **impervious**

a term denoting the resistance to penetration by water or plant roots.

■ **import**

water piped or channelled into an area.

■ **impoundment**

a body of water such as a pond, confined by a dam, dike, floodgate or other barrier. It is used to collect and store water for future use.

■ **impoundment**

a body of water or sludge confined by a dam, dike, floodgate, or other barrier.

■ **impregnate**

to coat, saturate, and/or surround the fibres of a reinforcing mat or fabric with an enveloping liquid material, (e.g., bitumen, elastomeric compound, etc.).

■ **incompatibility**

descriptive of two or more materials which are not suitable to be used together.

■ **independent variable**

a parameter of the system, which varies independently of other system parameters.

■ **index of refraction**

see **refractive index.**

■ **inertance, hydraulic**

a quantity related to the inertial forces required to accelerate or deceleration a fluid in a conduit or a passage. It is analogous to electrical inductance.

■ **inertial load**

the reaction force resulting from the acceleration of a mass and is equal to the product of the mass and the acceleration, and always acts in a direction opposite to that of the actuator motion.

■ **infiltration**

the gradual downward flow of water from the surface into soil material.

■ **influent**

the fluid flowing into a valve, filter or other devices.

■ **influent seepage**

the movement of gravity water in the zone of aeration from the ground surface toward the water table.

■ **infrared thermography**

a practice of roof system analysis where an infrared camera is used to measure the temperature differential of a roof surface to locate areas of underlying wet or moist insulation. (See **thermal image.**)

■ **ingested contaminant**

environmental contaminant that ingresses due to the action of the system (across reservoir breathers, pulled in by the drag action of rod and wiper seals, etc).

■ **inhibitor**

any substance, which slows, prevents, or modifies chemical reactions such as corrosion or oxidation.

■ **Initial Rate Of Absorption / IRA**

the weight of water absorbed expressed in grams per 30 sq. in. of contact surface when a brick is partially immersed for one minute. Also called suction. originally the IRA was limited by the BIA standard. it limited the IRA of brick at the time of laying to a maximum .025 oz per sq in. per min (approximately 20 g /30 sq in./ min).

■ **in-line wingwall**

a wingwall that is parallel to the centerline of bearings.

■ **inorganic chemicals/ compounds**

chemical substances of mineral origin, not of basically carbon structure. These include metals such as lead and cadmium.

■ **input**

an incoming signal (pressure, flow, etc.) to a control system or device, which initiates a hydraulic process.

■ **INR (Impact Noise Rating)**

a single figure rating which provides an estimate of the impact sound insulating performance of a floor-ceiling assembly.

■ **inside drain**

a roof drain positioned on a roof at some location other than the perimeter. It drains surface water inside the building through closed pipes to a drainage system.

■ **in-situ biodegradation**

treatment of soil in place to encourage contaminants to breakdown. It involves aerating the soil and adding nutrients to promote growth of microorganisms.

■ **in-situ vitrification**

a technology used to treat hazardous waste in soils. This process electrically melts the waste media at extremely high temperatures then allows it to cool, creating an extremely stable, insoluble, glasslike solid. The contaminants are destroyed or immobilised and the total volume of material is reduced.

■ **instability**

a time dependent increase in output without a corresponding increase in the input. Many special definitions of stability have been introduced for non-linear systems.

■ **instrinsic semiconductor**

a semiconductor material for which the electrical behaviour is characteristic of the pure material.

■ **insulation**

material which slows down or retards the flow or transfer of heat.

■ **insulation board, rigid**

a structural building board made of coarse wood or cane fibre in $1/2$ and $25/32$-inch thickness. It can be obtained in various size sheets, in various densities, and with several treatments.

■ **insulation fasteners**

any of several specialised mechanical fasteners designed to hold insulation down to a steel or a nailable deck.

■ **insulation vent**

a vent placed into the insulation which extends above the burm.

■ **insulation, thermal**

any material high in resistance to heat transmission that, when placed in the walls, ceiling, or floors of a structure, will reduce the rate of heat flow.

■ **insulator (electrical)**

a non-metallic material that has filled valence band at 0 K and a relatively wide energy band gap.

■ **integral abutment**

an abutment constructed as a rigid connection between the deck and primary support members of the superstructure and a single row of piles supporting the substructure.

■ **intensifier**

a device, which amplifies or increases the pressure over that of the source pressure and applies it to a particular section of a system at the cost of reduced flow rate. Also see **booster** and **amplifier.**

■ **intensive survey**

an analysis of loadings to a stream segment.

■ **interaction**

mutual (or reciprocal) action or influence.

■ **interior finish**

material used to cover the interior framed areas, or materials of walls and ceilings.

■ **intermediate course**

any layer between the wearing course and the base.

■ **intermetallic**

a compound of two metals that has a distinct chemical formula. The bonds in intermetallic compounds are often partly ionic.

■ **intermittent stream**

a stream, which has a period of zero flow for at least one week during most years. Where flow records are available, a stream with a 7Q2 flow of less than 0.1 cubic feet per second is considered intermittent.

■ **internal pressure**

pressure inside a building that is a function of ventilating equipment, wind velocity, and the number and location of openings and air leaks.

■ **interply**

between two layers of roofing felts that have been laminated together.

■ **interstate water**

according to law, waters are defined as 1. rivers, lakes and other waters that flow across or form a part of state or international boundaries; 2. waters of the Great Lakes; 3. coastal waters whose scope has been defined to include ocean waters seaward to the territorial limits and waters along the coastline (including inland streams) influenced by the tide.

■ **interstlces**

the void portion of rock or soil occupied by air or water.

■ **invariant point**

a point on a binary phase diagram at which three phases are in equilibrium.

■ **IRMA**

Insulated (or inverted) Roof Membrane Assembly. In this system the roof membrane is laid directly on the roof deck, covered with extruded foam insulation and ballasted with stone, minimum of 1000 lbs. per square.

■ **iron**

a chemical element (Fe); one of the cheapest and most used metals.

■ **irrigation**

the controlled application of water for cultural purposes through man-made systems to supply water requirements not satisfied by rainfall.

■ **irrigation efficiency**

the percentage of water applied, and which can be accounted for, in the soil moisture increase for consumptive use.

■ **irrigation return flow**

the applied irrigation, water, which is not consumptively used by plants and returns to a surface or ground water supply. Under conditions of water right litigation, the definition may restricted to measurable water returning to the stream from which it was diverted.

■ **irrigation water**

water, which is applied to assist crops in areas where rainfall is inadequate.

■ **isentropic**

a reversible adiabatic process.

■ **ISO**

International Organisation for Standardisation.

■ **isobaric**

refers to constant pressure conditions.

■ **isochoric**

refers to a change that takes place at constant volume.

■ **isotactic**

a type of polymer chain configuration wherein all side groups are positioned on the same side of the chain molecule.

■ **isothermal**

compression or expansion occurring at a constant temperature, as opposed to the adiabatic process.

■ **isotope**

atoms of the same element having different masses.

■ **izod impact test**

one of two tests that may be used to measure the impact energy of standard notched specimen.

■ **jack**

a single-acting cylinder that can be pressure actuated in only one direction.

■ **jack arch**

a multi-beam bridge having a concrete deck spanning between the beams formed in the shape of arches that originate from the bottom flanges and encasing most, if not all, of the beams. Jack arches are extremely strong, and nearly impossible to rehabilitate.

■ **jack rafter**

a rafter that spans the distance from the wall plate to a hip, or from a valley to a ridge.

More disposable housing! Opposing jack rafters cut short of the valley rafter.

■ **jacking**

mechanical lifting or sliding of an element or group of elements.

■ **jamb**

the side and head lining of a doorway, window, or other opening.

■ **jaw face**

in tensile testing machines, the surface of a jaw that, in the absence of a liner, contacts the specimen.

■ **jaw liner**

in tensile testing machines, a material placed between the jaw face and the specimen to improve the holding power of jaws.

■ **jaws**

in tensile testing machines, the elements of a clamp that grip the specimen.

■ **jerk-in**

in woven fabric, an extra filling thread dragged into the shed with the regular pick and extending only part of the way across the cloth. Also known as lash-in and pull-in

■ **jetty**

a structure extended into a sea, lake, or river to influence the current or tide or to protect a harbour.

■ **joint**

1. the space between the adjacent surfaces of two members or components joined and held together by nails, glue, cement, mortar, or other means.
2. a device connecting two or more adjacent parts of a structure; a roller joint allows adjacent parts to move controllably past one another; a rigid joint prevents adjacent parts from moving or rotating past one another.

■ **joint cement**

a powder that is usually mixed with water and used for joint treatment in gypsum-wallboard finish. Often called 'spackle'.

■ **joist**

1. one of a series of parallel beams, usually 2 inches in thickness, used to support floor and ceiling loads, and supported in turn by larger beams, girders, or bearing walls.
2. a horizontally placed timber or beam set on edge to give support to a floor or ceiling.

■ **kaolinite**

a finely divided crystalline form of hydrated aluminium silicate occurring as minute monoclinic crystals with a perfect basal cleavage

■ **Karl Fischer reagent**

a methanol solution of iodine, sulphur dioxide and pyridine used for determining the water content of resins.

■ **Kesternich test**

simulates acid rain conditions by subjecting test specimens to a sulphur dioxide atmosphere as well as condensing moisture for the purpose of evaluating rust/corrosion characteristics.

■ **kettle**

equipment used for heating bitumen to a flowing consistency.

■ **kick hole**

a defect frequently found in perimeter flashings arising from being stepped on or kicked. A small fracture of the base flashing in the area of the cant.

■ **kiln dried lumber**

lumber that has been kiln dried often to a moisture content of 6 to 12 percent. Common varieties of softwood lumber, such as framing lumber are dried to a somewhat higher moisture content.

■ **kilowatt-hour (kWh)**

a measure of electric usage equivalent to the use of 1,000 watts for one hour.

■ **kinetic energy**

the energy that a substance or body possesses by virtue of its mass (weight) and velocity.

■ **kitchen recycling centre**

a built-in section of the kitchen cabinetry that allows convenient separation of recyclable materials.

■ **knee cap**

a metal cover trim that fits over a panel rib after it has been cut and bent.

■ **knot**

in lumber, the portion of a branch or limb of a tree that appears on the edge or face of the piece.

■ **kraft**

a heavy water resistant paper.

■ **ladder polymers**

polymers comprising chains made up of fused rings. Examples are cyclised (acid-treated) rubber and polybutadiene. Also known as double stranded polymers.

■ **ladder, fixed**

a ladder which is permanently attached to a building.

■ **lag**

the quantity that an output is behind the input, normally measured in degrees.

■ **lag time**

the time from the centre of a unit storm to the peak discharge or centre of volume of the corresponding unit hydrograph.

■ **lagoon**

a shallow pond where sunlight, bacterial action, and oxygen work to purify waste water. Lagoons are typically used for the storage of waste waters, sludges, liquid wastes, or spent nuclear fuel.

■ **lakes**

an inland body of water, usually fresh water, formed by glaciers, river drainage etc., larger than a pool or pond. Bodies of water filling depressions in the earth's surface.

■ **lamellar structures**

plate-like single crystals which exist in some crystalline polymers.

■ **landfarm**

to apply waste to land and/or incorporate waste into the surface soil, such as fertiliser or soil conditioner. This practice is commonly used for disposal of composted wastes.

■ **landfill**

a disposal facility where waste is placed in or on land.

■ **landing**

a platform between flights of stairs or at the termination of a flight of stairs.

■ **lap**

the relative axial position relationship between the fixed and movable flow metering edges with the spool at null. Lap is measured as the total separation at zero flow of straight line extensions of the nearly straight portions of the normal flow curve, drawn separately for each polarity, expressed as per cent of rated input parameter.

■ **lap cement**

an asphalt-based roof cement formulated to adhere overlapping plies or asphalt roll roofing.

■ **lap seam**

occurs where overlapping materials are seamed, sealed, or otherwise bonded.

■ **lapping-in**

polishing a surface such as a valve seat to obtain a smooth mating surface.

■ **laser**

an acronym for light amplification by stimulated emission of radiation.

■ **latent heat**

the heat required to cause a material to undergo a change of phase.

■ **lateral**

small irrigation canal.

■ **lateral bracing**

bracing spanning diagonally between the bottom flanges of adjacent girders.

■ **lateral movement**

horizontal movement of a structure or part of it, earth, etc.

■ **lateral support**

vertical or horizontal means of bracing walls by columns, pilasters, cross walls, beams, floors, roofs, etc.

■ **latex**

a colloidal dispersion of a polymer or elastomer in water which coagulates into a film upon evaporation of the water.

■ **lath**

a building material of wood, metal, gypsum, or insulating board that is fastened to the frame of a building to act as a plaster base.

■ **lattice**

a framework of crossed wood or metal strips.

■ **lattice parameter**

the combination of unit cell edge lengths and interaxial angles that defines the unit cell geometry.

■ **leaching**

the process by, which soluble materials in the soil, such as nutrients, pesticide chemicals or contaminants, are washed into a lower layer of soil or are dissolved and carried away by water.

■ **lead**

1. soft and heavy metallic element used since roman times.
2. short, insulated electrical conductor.
3. the section of masonry wall built up as a guide for laying the balance of the wall. A line is attached to leads as a guide for constructing a wall between them.
4. hanging (usually vertical) guide beam that aligns the hammer and the pile.
5. the distance a screw thread advances in one complete turn.

■ **leader head**

see **conductor head.**

■ **leak**

that amount of fluid emitting from a component sufficient to cause rejection and, which performs no useful work.

■ **leakage, centre position**

this refers to the amount of leakage associated with spool lap conditions for a given clearance.

■ **lean-to-roof**

the sloping roof of a building addition having its rafters or supports pitched against and supported by the adjoining wall of a building.

■ **learning control system**

a system designed to recognise familiar features and patterns of a situation and then, based on its past experience or learned behaviour, react in an optimum manner.

■ **least-toxic**

this characterisation of a building material for the Green Builder Program indicates that urea formaldehyde is not present and/or VOC contents are minimal and/or water-based constituents are used. Products that have been certified to be "least-toxic" by certification groups such as Creen Cross, Green Shield, and Eco-Logo qualify for the Green Builder Program.

■ **ledger strip**

a strip of lumber nailed along the bottom of the side of a girder on which joists rest.

■ **leeward**

the opposite direction from which the wind is blowing. The side sheltered from the wind.

■ **let-in brace**

nominal 1 inch-thick boards applied into notched studs diagonally.

■ **letting**

opening of the project bids to determine the low bid.

■ **levee**

a natural or man-made earthen obstruction along the edge of a stream, lake, or river. Usually used to restrain the flow of water out of a river bank.

■ **level or sight gauge**

a device for indicating the amount of fluid contained in a reservoir.

■ **lever rule**

mathematical expression whereby the relative phase amounts in a two-phase alloy at equilibrium my be computed.

■ **leverage**

a gain in output force over input force by sacrificing the distance moved. Mechanical advantage or force multiplication.

■ **LFD**

Load Factor Design.

■ **life cycle**

a life cycle assessment (LCA) is an objective process to evaluate all the environmental burdens of a product or process through its entire existence. This encompasses extracting and processing raw materials, manufacturing, transportation, distribution, use and maintenance, recycling and final disposal.

■ **life cycle costing (LCC)**

all phases through which an item passes from the time it is initially developed until it is either deemed unserviceable in its current state and use or disposed as being excess.

■ **life cycling costing**

a method of economic analysis that takes into account expected costs over the useful life of an asset.

■ **life, operating**

the useful life of a device or system expressed in terms of cycles of operation, hours or similar units.

■ **lift**

the height a body or column of fluid is raised; e.g., from the reservoir fluid level to the pump inlet. Lift is sometimes used to express a negative pressure or vacuum. The opposite of head.

■ **light**

space in a window sash for a single pane of glass.

■ **light detection and ranging (LIDAR)**

LIDAR is a new technology that uses lasers to measure the elevation of the ground and provides the greatest possible detail of elevations throughout all of Harris County. LIDAR provides a ground elevation point every 15 feet that is accurate to +/- 6 inches.

■ **light duty pavement**

pavement designed for low traffic volumes and light loads.

■ **light water reactor (lwr)**

a power plant, which uses ordinary water as distinguished from one that uses heavy water. Fission energy is released in the form of heat and is transferred to a conventional steam cycle, which generates electric energy.

■ **lime**

1. various classes of calcium oxide alone or in combinations with magnesium oxide, containing impurities such as silica, iron, aluminium oxide, etc. This lime is industrially produced by obtained by calcining forms of calcium carbonate (as shells or limestone), with the final product a white caustic lumpy powder which is used as an industrial alkali, construction

materials (such as plasticisers for mortar or plaster), etc. Also known as quicklime or unslaked lime.
2. quicklime to which sufficient water has been added as to convert the oxides to hydroxides, primarily to calcium hydroxide, a white crystalline strong alkali, $Ca(OH)_2$, that is used especially to make mortar and plaster and to soften water.

■ **lime putty**

the plastic material resulting after the lime hydration process stops and the semi-fluid mass cools off. In this form the hydrated lime is ready to be added to masonry mortar mixes (as a plasticiser) or can be used by itself as either base or finish coat plaster, especially in historical restorations.

■ **lime, hydrated**

quicklime to which sufficient water has been added as to convert the oxides to hydroxides. This reaction, called slaking, develops sufficient heat to bring the entire semi fluid mass to a boil.

■ **limestone**

limestone's are sedimentary rocks consisting mainly of calcite (calcium carbonate) and/or dolomite (calcium magnesium carbonate), they are usually formed from fragments of shell, coral and other marine organisms, some finely grained and compact limestones - for example, oolite are created from chemical precipitates. Sometimes called greystone, limestones were popular for building because they combined relatively easy

workability with good weather resistance, sulphur oxides in today's acid rain converts limestone to friable gypsum however.

Limestone - Crystalline

■ **limit states design**

a method of design based on the strength or serviceability limits of the material and the predictability of the applied loads.

■ **line**

a tube, pipe or hose, which acts as a conductor of hydraulic fluid. Conduits are expressed as a pressure line, suction line, bypass line, drain line, etc.

■ **linear**

a straight line relationship between two variables.

■ **linear actuator**

a device, which converts pressure energy into linear motion with a limited stroke; i.e., a hydraulic cylinder or ram.

■ **linear equation (function)**

an equation of the first degree (which always maps as a straight line).

■ **linearity**

a measure of deviation from proportional relationship in the ratio of valve output to input. The degree to, which the normal flow curve conforms to the normal flow gain line with other operational variables held constant. When output varies in direct proportion to the input, the valve is considered linear.

■ **lintel**

beam placed over an opening in a wall. A horizontal structural member that supports the load over an opening such as a door or window.

■ **liquid**

a state of matter, neither gas nor solid, that flows and takes the shape of its container.

■ **liquid-applied membrane**

generally applied to cast-in-place concrete surfaces in one or more coats to provide fully-adhered waterproof membranes which conform to all contours.

■ **live loads**

temporary loads that the roof structure must be designed to support, as required by governing building codes. Live loads are generally moving and/or dynamic or environmental, (e.g., people, installation equipment, wind, snow, ice or rain, etc.).

■ **LL+I**

live load plus impact.

■ **llmnology**

that branch of hydrology pertaining to the study of lakes.

■ **load**

weight distribution throughout a structure; loads caused by wind, earthquakes, and gravity, for example, affect how weight is distributed throughout a structure.

■ **load locus**

a diagram that defines the complete boundary of the load for a given application or load situation. It possesses valuable properties useful in specifying components to match the load.

■ **load plate**

a horizontal plate that transmits a vertical force through it's thickness.

■ **load pressure**

the pressure generated by an externally applied force.

■ **load rating**

a value that indicates the live load capacity of a bridge.

■ **load sensing system**

a closed-circuit system with load/pressure feedback. It combines the advantages of an open-centre system and constant pressure closed-centre systems while avoiding their major disadvantages.

■ **lock down seal**

a reseal to prevent further loss of aggregate if original seal is experiencing aggregate loss. Normally 5 mm or 7 mm aggregate. Also referred to as pin down seal.

■ **logic**

the interrelation or sequence of events or facts required to achieve a predictable and specific outcome.

■ **longevity**

long duration of useful life or that part of a component's, equipment's or system's service life that lies between the phases of early failure and wear-out failure.

■ **long-term remedial phase**

distinct, often incremental, steps that are taken to solve site pollution problems. Depending on the complexity, site cleanup activities can be separated into a number of these phases.

■ **lookout**

a short wood bracket or cantilever to support an overhang portion of a roof or the like, usually concealed from view.

■ **loose laid**

a membrane 'laid loosely', i.e., not adhered, over a roof deck.

■ **loose-laid membranes**

membranes that are not attached to the substrate except at the perimeter of the roof and at penetrations. Typically, loose-laid membranes are held in place with ballast, such as water-worn stone, gravel, pavers, etc.

■ **louver**

an opening with a series of horizontal slats so an ranged as to permit ventilation but to exclude rain, sunlight, or vision.

■ **LRFD**

load and resistance factor design.

■ **LS**

length of spiral.

■ **lubricity**

the ability of a lubricant to minimise friction between mating surfaces under boundary lubrication conditions and moderate loading, oiliness.

■ **lumber**

lumber is the product of the sawmill and planning mill not further manufactured other than by sawing, re-sawing, and passing lengthwise through a standard planning machine, crosscutting to length, and matching.

■ **lumber, boards**

yard lumber less than 2 inches thick and 2 or more inches wide.

■ **lumber, dimension**

yard lumber from 2 inches to, but not including, 5 inches thick and 2 or more inches wide. Includes joists, rafters, studs, plank, and small timbers.

■ **lumber, dressed size**

the dimension of lumber after shrinking from green dimension and after machining to size or pattern.

■ **lumber, matched**

lumber that is dressed and shaped on one edge in a grooved pattern and on the other in a tongued pattern.

■ **lumber, shiplap**

lumber that is edge-dressed to make a close rabbet or lapped joint.

■ **lumber, timbers**

yard lumber 5 or more inches in least dimension. Includes beams, stringers, posts, caps, sills, girders, and purling.

■ **lumber, yard**

lumber of those grades, sizes, and patterns which are generally intended for ordinary construction, such as framework and rough coverage of houses.

■ **lumped parameter model**

a mathematical model, which treats all variables of a system element (lumped) as if they acted at only one point in the element. The converse is a distributed system.

■ **M&PT**

maintenance and protection of traffic. The control plan for traffic through a construction site.

■ **M.S.E.S.**

mechanically stabilised earth structure.

■ **macadam**

refers to a pavement type generally consisting of large single size aggregate with a surface layer of smaller material with or without binder to lock the surface together. Can be either a bitumen based or water based macadam pavement.

■ **machinability**

a measure of the ease with which a material can be shaped with abrasive or cutting tools.

■ **machinability index**

a relative measure of the machinability of a material under specified standard conditions.

■ **macromolecule**

a huge molecule made up of thousands of atoms.

■ **magmatlc water**

water driven out of magma during crystallisation.

■ **magnetic field strength**

the intensity of an externally applied magnetic field.

■ **magnetic flux density**

the magnetic field produced in a substance by an external magnetic field.

■ **magnetic induction**

see **magnetic flux density**.

■ **magnetic lock**

a motion impediment produced by an unshielded magnetic field attracting and accumulating ferromagnetic particles that induce surface lockup.

■ **magnetic susceptibility**

the proportionality constant between the magnetisation M and the magnetic field strength H.

■ magnetisation

the total magnetic moment per unit volume of material. Also, a measure of the contribution to the magnetic flux by some material within an H field.

■ maintenance

the art of ensuring that the performance of a component, equipment or system is kept within a set of predetermined limits. All actions necessary for retaining an item in, or restoring it to, a serviceable condition and includes servicing, repair, modification, overhaul, inspection, and condition verification.

■ major flooding

flood conditions resulting in extensive inundation and property damage. Typically characterised by the evacuation of people and livestock and the closure of both primary and secondary roads.

■ manifold

a fluid conduit, which has multiple inlets and multiple connection ports and possibly various interconnections.

■ mansard

a decorative steep-sloped roof on the perimeter of a building.

■ mansard roof

a roof which rises by inclined planes from all four sides of a building. The sloping roofs on all four sides have two pitches, the lower pitch usually very steep and the upper pitch less steep.

■ mantel

the shelf above a fireplace. Also used in referring to the decorative trim around a fireplace opening.

■ manual control

a control method, which requires the physical effort of the operator; e.g., a lever or foot pedal control for a valve.

■ manual override

a means of manually operating an automatic control.

■ marble

geologically, marble refers to certain crystalline rocks composed primarily of calcite or dolomite-metamorphosed limestone. In the stone and construction industries on the other hand, the term "marble" refers to any rock that can take a high polish. This even includes a few lime stones and granites. The purest from is white statuary marble, best exemplified by product mined in the Carrara area of Italy. Commonly found marbles contain various impurities which produce a whole spectrum of patterns and colours. Because is softer than most other construction stones, marble can be worked more easily and is used mainly for ornamentation. The downfall is that marbles are often more expensive. They also tend to be sensitive to exposure to atmospheric pollutants and acids from any source, so many are not suitable for exterior use even when protective transparent coatings are used.

■ **martensite**

a metastable Fe-C composition consisting of supersaturated carbon in iron that is the product of a diffusionless (athermal) transformation from austenite.

■ **mason**

to the french maçon (latin matio or machio), 'a builder of walls' or 'a stone-cutter'.

■ **masonry**

brick, stone, concrete, hollow-tile, concrete-block, gypsum block, or other building units, bonded together with mortar (usually).

■ **masonry cement**

a mill-mixed cementitious material to which sand and water must be added.

■ **masonry plate**

the bottom steel plate that connects the bridge bearing to the pedestal.

■ **masonry unit**

natural or manufactured building units of burned clay, concrete, stone, glass, gypsum, etc. Hollow masonry unit: one whose net cross-sectional area in any plane parallel to the bearing surface is less than 75 percent of the gross. Modular masonry unit: one whose nominal dimensions are based on the 4 inches module. Solid masonry unit: one whose net cross-sectional area in every plane parallel to the bearing surface is 75 percent or more of the gross.

■ **mastic**

1. a pasty material used as a cement (as for setting tile) or a protective coating (as for thermal insulation or waterproofing).
2. a heavy trowel applied bitumen used for flashings or patch work which remains elastic and pliable.

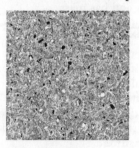

■ **mastic asphalt**

a mixture of bitumen and fines that can be used for waterproofing in building and industrial applications.

■ **material safety data sheets**

a written description of the chemicals in a product, and pertinent other data including such things as safe handling and emergency procedures. In accordance with OSHA regulations, it is the manufacturer's responsibility to produce an MSDS and the employer's responsibility to communicate its contents to employees.

mathematical model

an equation or set of equations, which describe the behaviour of a system or component with respect to an independent variable or variables.

matrix

the body constituent of a composite or two-phase alloy that completely surrounds the dispersed phase and gives the body its bulk form.

matter

anything, which is solid, liquid or gas, and has mass.

maximum density

the maximum density that could be achieved in a sample of asphalt if it were possible to compact it so as to exclude all air voids between coated aggregate particles (also know as void-free density).

measuring and inspection gauges

precision-made mass production tooling used by semi-skilled factory workers to test and/or check mass produced components for conformance to engineering requirements and specification, often to very high levels of dimensional and/or form accuracy.

mechanical control

any control actuated by linkages, gears, screws, cams or other mechanical elements.

mechanical lock

an asperity induced lockup or seizure of two mating surfaces in relative motion.

mechanically-fastened membranes

generally used to describe membranes that have been attached at defined intervals to the substrate. Mechanical fastening may be performed with various fasteners and/or other mechanical devices, such as plates or battens.

median stream flow (median hydro)

the rate of discharge of a stream for, which there are equal numbers of greater and lesser flow occurrences during a specified period.

melt point

the temperature at which the solid asphalt becomes a liquid.

melting

the changing of a solid into a liquid.

melting point

the temperature at which a solid substance changes to a liquid state.

meltwater

water that comes from the melting ice of a glacier or a snowbank.

membrane

a generic term relating to a variety of sheet goods used for certain built-up roofing repairs and application. Also used to describe the combination of felts and mopping of bitumen forming a single flexible unit and waterproofing system of a bur.

■ **memorandum of under-standing**

an interagency agreement defining which agency has a responsibility.

■ **mer**

the group of atoms that constitutes a polymer chain repeat unit.

■ **metal**

the electropositive elements and alloys based on these elements.

■ **metal die-casting die**

a piece of precision-made mass production tooling used to mould molten metals such as lead, zinc, aluminium, copper and brass into shapes such as fishing sinkers, electric motor end frames, engine pistons, and carburettor components.

■ **metal edge**

brake metal or metal extrusions which are secured at the perimeter of burm to form a weather tight seal.

■ **metal extrusion die**

a piece of precision-made mass production tooling used to extrude long continuous metal shapes of uniform cross section such as copper, brass, or aluminium tubing, aluminium guttering, brass or copper wire, rod and bar, and steel beams, rods and angle irons

■ **metal flashing**

accessory components fabricated from sheet metal and used to weath-erproof terminating roof covering edges. Frequently used as through-wall flashing, cap flashing (coping), counterflashing, step-flashing, etc. (See **flashing.**)

■ **metal lath**

sheets of metal that are slit and drawn out to form openings. Used as a plaster base for walls and ceilings and as reinforcing over other forms of plaster base.

■ **metastable**

non-equilibrium state that may persist for a very long time.

■ **meteoric water**

new water derived from the atmosphere.

■ **meteorology**

the science of the atmosphere; the study of atmospheric phenomena.

■ **methane (CH_4)**

an odourless, colourless, flammable gas that is a major constituent of natural gas. It is a more powerful global warming agent than carbon dioxide.

■ **meter**

to regulate the rate of flow of fluid in a circuit.

■ **metre-in**

to regulate the flow of fluid entering an actuator or system.

■ **metre-out**

to regulate the flow of fluid exiting an actuator or system.

■ **mg/l**

milligrams per litre.

■ **micro-surfacing**

a bituminous slurry surfacing, usually containing polymer, which is capable of being spread in variably thick layers for rut-filling and correction courses, and for wearing course applications requiring good surface texture.

■ **micron (or micrometre)**

one thousandth part of one mm, 0.0000394-in., or one-millionth of a metre. a common unit used when specifying filters, sieves and screens.

■ **microstructure**

the structural features of an alloy that are subject to observation under a microscope.

■ **migration**

the movement of oil, gas, contaminants, water, or other liquids through porous and permeable rock.

■ **mil**

a unit of measure, one mil is equal to 0.001 inches or 25.400 microns, often used to indicate the thickness of a roofing membrane.

■ **military loading**

a loading arrangement that simulates heavy military vehicles.

■ **miller indices**

a set of three integers that designate crystallographic planes, as determined from reciprocals of fractional axial intercepts.

■ **miller-bravis indices**

a set of four integers that designate crystallographic planes in hexagonal crystals.

■ **millwork**

generally all building materials made of finished wood and manufactured in millwork plants and planking mills are included under the term 'millwork'. It includes such items as inside and outside doors, window and doorframes, blinds, porch work, mantels, panel work, stairways, mouldings, and interior trim. It normally does not include flooring, ceiling, or siding.

■ **mineral**

any naturally occurring inorganic element or chemical compound. Rocks are a compound of minerals.

■ **mineral fibre**

inorganic fibres of glass, asbestos, or rock (mineral wool).

■ **mineral spirits**

a by-product of petroleum, clear in colour, a solvent for asphaltic coatings.

■ **mineral surfaced**

a heavy roofing felt that has very small granules embedded across its surface.

■ **mineral-surfaced roofing**

roofing materials whose surface or top layer consists of mineral granules.

■ **minimum streamflow**

the specific amount of water reserved to support aquatic life, to minimise pollution, or for recreation. It is subject to the priority system and does not affect water rights established prior to its institution.

■ **minor losses**

these losses occur when flow is suddenly expanded or contracted.

■ **miter joint**

the joint of two pieces at an angle that bisects the joining angle. For example, the miter joint at the side and head casing at a door opening is made at a 45° angle.

■ **mitigation**

when used in the context of environmental assessments, it refers to an action designed to lessen or reduce adverse impacts.

■ **mixed dislocation**

a dislocation that has both edge and screw components.

■ **mixing plants**

refer batch plant.

■ **Mn**

manganese.

■ **modified asphalt**

an asphalt where a binder has been modified by the addition of rubber, polymers, fibres etc.. For specific applications.

■ **modified bitumen**

bitumen modified by special processing, generally with the addition of SBS type rubber or Atactic Polypylenes (APP). Some are non-reinforced, while others are reinforced with polyester, polyvinyl acetate, fibreglass, polypropylene or aluminium foil.

■ **modular joint**

a type of superstructure deck sealing system that is able to accommodate large thermal movements and rotations.

■ **modulus of elasticity**

the ratio of stress to strain for a material under perfectly elastic deformation.

■ **modulus, rubber (or elastomer)**

the stress level at a predetermined elongation, usually reported at 100%. It is a good indicator of compound toughness and at a given hardness, high modulus generally means good anti-extrusion and dynamic characteristics.

■ **moisture**

essentially water, quantitatively (and sometimes qualitatively) determined by definite prescribed methods which may vary according to the nature of the material.

■ **moisture barrier**

a special building paper fastened over the sheathing on the inside face of the cavity. It is lapped and taped to provide a third level of protection against moisture penetration.

■ **moisture content**

term which in engineering indicates the percentage moisture content (which equals the weight of moisture divided by the weight of dry material multiplied by 100). The moisture content of a concrete aggregate, soil or mineral sample consists of two portions, namely, the free or surface moisture which can be removed by exposure to air, and the inherent moisture which is entrapped in the material, and is removed by heating at a specific temperature.

■ **moisture content of wood**

weight of the water contained in the wood, usually expressed as a percentage of the weight of the oven dry wood.

■ **moisture relief vent**

a venting device installed through the roofing membrane to relieve moisture vapour pres-sure from within the roofing system.

■ **moisture scan**

the use of a mechanical device (infrared, or nuclear) to detect the presence of moisture within a roof assembly. (See non-destructive testing.)

■ **mole run**

a meandering buckle or ridging in a roof membrane not associated with insulation or deck joints.

■ **molecule**

a very small bit of matter. The smallest amount of a compound, which has all the properties of the compound.

■ **monitor**

a large structure rising above the surrounding roof planes, designed to give light and/or ventilation to the building interior.

■ **monitor, saw-tooth**

a type of monitor characterised by sharp angled pitches and vertical sections, usually arranged in rows much like teeth of a saw.

■ **monolithic dome**

a dome composed of a series of arches, joined together with a series of horizontal rings called parallels.

■ **monomer**

a molecule consisting of a single mer.

■ **mop-and-flop**

an application procedure in which roofing elements (insulation boards, felt plies, cap sheets, etc.) are initially placed upside down adjacent to their ultimate locations, are coated with adhesive or bitumen, and are then turned over and applied to the substrate.

■ **mopping**

a layer of hot bitumen mopped between plies of roofing felt.

■ **mopping, full**

the application of bitumen by mopping in such a manner that the surface being mopped is entirely coated with a reasonably uniform coating.

■ **mopping, spot**

the procedure of applying hot bitumen in a random fashion of small daubs, as compared to full mopping.

■ **mopping, sprinkle**

a special application of installing insulation to the decks. It is done by dipping a roof mop into hot bitumen and sprinkling the material onto the deck.

■ **mopping, strip**

the application of bitumen in parallel bands.

■ **mortar**

a plastic mixture of cementitious materials, fine aggregate and water.
1. fat mortar: mortar containing a high percentage of cementitious components. It is a sticky mortar which adheres to a trowel.
2. high-bond mortar: mortar which develops higher bond strengths with masonry units than normally developed with conventional mortar.
3. lean mortar: mortar which is deficient in cementitious components, it is usually harsh and difficult to spread.

■ **mortise**

a slot cut into a board, plank, or timber, usually edgewise, to receive tenon of another board, plank, or timber to form a joint.

■ **MOSFET**

metal-oxide-silicon field effect transistor, an integrated circuit element.

■ **motor**

a device for converting electrical or fluid energy into rotary mechanical motion.

■ **motor, fixed-displacement**

a rotary motor in, which the displacement per revolution is not adjustable.

■ **motor, fluid**

a rotary-motor device for converting fluid energy into rotary motion, a rotary actuator.

■ **motor, limited rotary**

a rotary motor having limited angular motion or oscillation.

■ **motor, rotary**

a motor capable of continuous rotary motion and producing an output torque proportional to the displacement per revolution and the pressure drop between intake and discharge ports.

■ **motor, variable-displacement**

a rotary motor in, which the displacement per revolution is adjustable.

■ **motoring**

a condition caused by servo valve static friction, which requires an undesirable force application to stop the motion.

■ **moulding**

a wood strip having a coned or projecting surface used for decorative purposes.

■ **movable bridge**

a bridge in which the deck moves to clear a navigation channel; a swing bridge has a deck that rotates around a center point; a drawbridge has a deck that can be raised and lowered; a bascule bridge deck is raised with counterweights like a drawbridge; and the deck of a lift bridge is raised vertically like a massive elevator.

■ **MSxx**

designation for a metric design tractor truck with semi-trailer or the corresponding lane load. The xx is replaced with the weight of the design truck, in metric tons.

■ **mud cracks**

cracks developing from the normal shrinkage of an emulsion coating when applied too heavily.

■ **mullion**

a vertical bar or divider in the frame between windows, doors, or other openings.

■ **municipal sewage**

sewage from a community, which may be composed of domestic sewage, industrial wastes or both.

■ **muntin**

a small member which divides the glass or openings of sash or doors.

■ **Mxx**

designation for a metric design two-axle truck or the corresponding lane load. The xx is replaced with the weight of the design truck, in metric tons.

■ **N**

nitrogen.

■ **nace**

abbreviation for national association of corrosion engineers.

■ **nadic methyl anhydride**

an accelerator for epoxy resin.

■ **nail laminated**

a large timber member formed by nailing layers of smaller timber members together.

■ **nailer**

(commonly referred to as Blocking) a piece or pieces of dimensional lumber and/or plywood secured to the structural deck or walls, which provide a receiving medium for the fasteners used to attach membrane or flashing. Generally, it is recommended that nailers be the same thickness as the adjacent insulation, and may be treated with a non-oil-borne preservative, and be of sufficient width to fully support the horizontal flashing flange of a metal flashing (where used).

■ **natural finish**

a transparent finish which does not seriously alter the original colour or grain of the natural wood. Natural finishes are usually provided by sealers, oils, varnishes, water-repellent preservatives, and other similar materials.

■ **natural flow**

the rate of water movement past a specified point on a natural stream. The flow comes from a drainage area in, which there has been no stream diversion caused by storage, import, export, return flow, or change in consumptive use caused by man-controlled modifications to land use. Natural flow rarely occurs in a developed country.

■ **natural frequency**

the frequency of the cycling motion of an undamped second-order component. For a transient-response curve, the frequency of cycling, which the deviation would have if the response were undamped. Also the frequency at, which an object would vibrate at zero damping. On a Bode Plot of a second-order system, it is the frequency where the extension of the final slope of the response curve intersects the 0-db line of the amplitude ratio.

■ **natural linoleum**

cork is the primary material in natural linoleum. cork is from the bark of the cork tree and is harvested without destroying the trees.

■ **NCHRP**

National Cooperative Highway Research Program.

■ **neoprene**

a synthetic rubber (polychloroprene) used in liquid-applied and sheet-applied elastomeric roof membranes or flashings.

■ **net positive suction head**

the minimum suction head required for a pump to operate and this value depends on liquid characteristics, total liquid head, pump speed and capacity, and impeller design.

■ **net positive suction head required**

the NPSH required at pump suction port. If NPSHA is less than NPSHR, cavitation occurs.

■ **network polymer**

a polymer composed of trifunctional mer units that form three-dimensional molecules.

■ **neutralisation number**

a measure of the acidity of a fluid. It is defined as the milligrams of potassium hydroxide required to neutralise the acidity in one gram of fluid.

■ **newel**

a post to which the end of a stair railing or balustrade is fastened. Also, any post to which a railing or balustrade is fastened.

■ **Newt**

a unit of kinematic viscosity in the British system of units. One Newt is one square inch per second.

■ **Newtonian fluid**

a liquid in which viscosity is independent of the shear rate of the fluid.

■ **night seal (or night tie-off)**

a material and/or method used to temporarily seal a membrane edge during construction to protect the roofing assembly in place from water penetration. Usually removed when roofing application is resumed.

■ **nimbostratus clouds**

rain clouds in layers that are generally spread across the sky.

■ **nimbus clouds**

storm clouds that are usually dark in colour.

■ **nipple**

a short length of tubing or pipe used for joining conduit elements.

■ **nitrogen**

a nutrient present in ammonia, nitrate or nitrite or elemental form in water due possibly to non-point source pollution or improperly operating wastewater treatment plants.

■ **nitrogen oxide(NO)**

a colourless, poisonous gas. It is a by-product of gas combustion.

■ **nominal dimension**

a dimension greater than a specified masonry dimension by the thickness of a mortar joint, but not more than 1/2 in.

■ **nominal rating**

an arbitrary value assigned to a filter by the manufacturer and generally lacks reproducibility.

■ **nominal size**

a size designation of an aggregate that which gives an indication of the largest particle size present.

■ **nomograph**

a chart on, which a straight line can be drawn so as to intersect three scales in values that satisfy an equation or a given set of conditions.

■ **non-bearing wall**

a wall supporting no load other than its own weight.

■ **non-combustible material**

any material which will neither ignite nor actively support combustion in air at a temperature of 1200 °F when exposed to fire.

■ **non-consumptive use**

using water in a way that does not reduce the supply. Examples include hunting, fishing, boating, water-skiing, swimming, and some power production.

■ **non-contact recreation**

recreational pursuits not involving a significant risk of water ingestion, including fishing, commercial and recreational boating, and limited body contact incidental to shoreline activity.

■ **non-crystalline**

the solid state wherein there is no long-range atomic order. Sometimes used synonymously with the terms amorphous, glassy and vitreous.

■ **non-destructive**

a phrase describing a method of examining the interior of a component whereby no damage is done to the component itself.

■ **non-linearity**

an input-output relationship, which cannot be represented by a single straight line, e.g. hysteresis, deadband, coulomb friction, sharp edged orifice, etc.

■ **non-point source pollution**

forms of pollution caused by sediment, nutrients, organic and toxic substances originating from land use activities,, which are carried to lakes and streams by surface runoff. Non-point source pollution occurs when the rate of materials entering these waterbodies exceeds natural levels.

■ **non-porous**

something, which does not allow water to pass through it.

■ **non—return valve**

a valve, which normally allows flow in one direction only.

■ **normal crown**

the cross slope arrangement for a tangent roadway alignment.

■ **normally open**

a valve or other device, which allows fluid flow when there is no input signal. An input action must be applied to close the valve.

■ **nosing**

the projecting edge of a moulding or drip. Usually applied to the projecting moulding on the edge of a stair tread.

■ **notch**

a crosswise rabbet at the end of a board.

■ **nozzle**

a device used to shape a stream of fluid emerging from a line. It is used to convert pressure energy into velocity energy.

■ **nuclear density meter**

an instrument for the non-destructive determination of the density and moisture content of material using a radioactive source for its operation.

■ **nuclear meter**

a device used to detect moisture by measuring slowed, deflected neutrons.

■ **nuclear waste**

the radioactivity by-products and contaminated materials produced in nuclear powered electric generating facilities. There is no proven method for safely disposing of these wastes, some of which can be toxic for thousands of years.

■ **nucleation**

the initial stage in a phase transformation. It is evidenced by the formation of small particles (nuclei) of the new phase, which are capable of growing.

■ **null**

the condition where the valve supplies zero control flow at zero load pressure drop.

■ **o c, on centre**

the measurement of spacing for studs, rafters, joists, and the like in a building from the centre of one member to the centre of the next.

■ **o g, or ogee**

a moulding with a profile in the form of a letter s; having the outline of a reversed curve.

■ **OAW**

abbreviation for oxyacetylene welding.

■ **obliteration**

a process producing an obstructed flow path choked off by obliterants (polar materials such as water, long chain polymers and silica) that are attracted to the walls of the flow passage.

■ **ocean thermal gradients**

the temperature difference between deep and surface water in the oceans.

■ **oceanography**

the science relating to the study of the ocean.

■ **oceans**

the great bodies of salt water, which cover more than two-thirds of the earth's surface.

■ **octabromodiphenyl**

an additive to improve fire retardancy

■ **octahedral position**

the void space among closed-packed, hard sphere atoms or ions for which there are six nearest neighbours. An octahedron (double pyramid) is curcumscribed by lines constructed from centers of adjacent spheres.

■ **oil-canning**

the term describing distortion of thin-gauge metal panels which are fastened in a manner restricting normal thermal movement.

■ **oiliness**

that property of a lubricant, which produces low friction under conditions of boundary lubrication.

■ **oil-in-water**

a dispersion of oil in a continuous phase of water.

■ **old-growth**

wood from trees found in mature forests. In many cases, the trees have never been exposed to logging operations.

■ **omega rating**

a standard method of expressing the tolerance or sensitivity of a hydraulic component to contaminants in the hydraulic fluid. The OMEGA value corresponds to the Beta-Ten value of the filtration system needed to protect the pump for 1000 hours of service at rated conditions.

■ **open centre**

a condition where pump delivery recirculates freely to the reservoir in the centre or neutral position of the valve.

■ **open graded asphalt (open graded friction coarse)**

asphalt with a high percentage of air voids. Used in the wearing course to reduce surface water and traffic noise and to provide a higher skid resistance. Normally one size.

■ **open loop circuit**

a hydraulic circuit in which there is no automatic feedback to the control input signal.

■ operating conditions

operating conditions such as temperature and pressure numerical values relating to any given specific application of a unit. These may change during the course of operations.

■ operation and maintenance

1. activities conducted at a site after a Superfund site action is completed to ensure that the action is effective and operating properly.
2. actions taken after construction to assure that facilities constructed to treat waste water will be properly operated, maintained, and managed to achieve efficiency levels and prescribed effluent limitations in an optimum manner.

■ operator

notation used to simplify the writing of differential equations such as the Laplace operator.

■ optimal control system

a system where the control process is manipulated according to a 'performance index' defined by the user.

■ order

the highest order derivative, which occurs in the equation.

■ ordinary differential equation

a differential equation, which expresses the response of a system with respect to a single independent variable.

■ organic

a term designating any chemical compound which contains carbon and hydrogen.

■ organic chemicals/compounds

animal or plant- produced substances containing mainly carbon, hydrogen, and oxygen, such as benzene and toluene.

■ organic felt

an asphalt roofing base material manufactured from cellulose fibres.

■ organic waste

natural materials, such as food and yard waste, that decompose naturally.

■ organism

any living thing; either plant or animal.

■ oriflce

as used in water studies An opening with a closed perimeter; is usually sharp edged, and of regular form in a plate, wall, or partition through, which water may flow. An orifice is used for the measurement or control of water.

■ o-ring

a type of seal consisting of an elastomer in the shape of a toroid or donut. It is normally mounted in a groove in a manner that the effectiveness of sealing increases with pressure.

■ orthotropic deck

a lightweight decking system that uses closely spaced open or closed steel ribs and a horizontal steel deck plate.

■ **oscillatory**

a reciprocating type rotary motion also called limited rotation.

■ **outfall**

a designated outfall pursuant to a commission issued discharge permit or NPDES permit.

■ **outgas**

the emitting of fumes into the air.

■ **outrigger**

an extension of a rafter beyond the wall line. Usually a smaller member nailed to a larger rafter to form a cornice or roof overhang.

■ **outwash**

a deposit of sand and gravel formed by streams of meltwater flowing from a glacier.

■ **overhand work**

laying brick from inside a wall by men standing on a floor or on a scaffold.

■ **overhang**

that part of the roof structure which extends horizontally beyond the vertical plane of the exterior walls of a building.

■ **overhaul**

to overhaul a piece of equipment is to pull it apart, inspect it for damage, repair or replace damaged parts, then assemble the equipment and adjust so that it operates just as if it was new.

■ **overlay**

the addition of a layer over an existing pavement. Can be asphalt or crushed rock. Also referred to as re-sheeting.

■ **overshoot**

the exceeding or surpassing of a target value as operating conditions change.

■ **oxidation**

a chemical process in, which oxygen joins with metal atoms to form oxidation products (e.g., oxide coating),, which can cause changes in fluid properties.

■ **oxidation stability**

ability of substance to withstand chemical reaction with oxygen/air and subsequent degradation. A factor of prime importance in high temperature operation.

■ **oxidise**

to combine with oxygen in the air.

■ **ozone resistance**

the ability of a material to resist the deteriorating effects of ozone exposure.

■ **P**

phosphorous. A nutrient.

■ package

describes the method of supply of the roving yarn (that is, milk bottle package, twisted tube, etc.).

■ paint

mixture of a pigment which is dispersed into a liquid (called a vehicle) designed for application to a substrate when spread in one or more thin coats. These layers dry out to a solid film, adherent to the substrate. Paint is designed to protect and/or decorate the surface it is applied to. A combination of pigments with suitable thinners or oils to provide decorative and protective coatings.

■ painting

the act of applying a coating or paint film. Coating of a tunnel or mine roof with a coal-tar paint that seals the bottom strata of the roof to prevent air from entering the crevices of the roof.

■ panel

in house construction, a thin flat piece of wood, plywood, or similar material, framed by stiles and rails as in a door or fitted into grooves of thicker material with moulded edges for decorative wall treatment.

■ panel wall

exterior, non-load bearing wall wholly supported at each story. Panel walls are required to be self-supporting between stories. They must resist lateral forces such as wind pressures and must transfer these forces to adjacent structural members.

■ paper building

a general term for papers, felts, and similar sheet materials used in buildings without reference to their properties or uses.

■ paper sheathing

a building material, generally paper or felt, used in wall and roof construction as a protection against the passage of air and sometimes moisture.

■ paramagnetism

a relatively weak form of magnetism that results from the independent alignment of atomic dipoles (magnetic) with an applied magnetic field.

■ parameter

restrictive factor. In engineering, a parameter may be a constant value in an equation or one of a set of measurable factors (such as humidity, temperature, colour, or acidity) that define a system and determine or limits its behaviour.

■ parapet wall

a low wall around the perimeter of a roof deck.

■ **parge coat**

a thin application of plaster for coating a wall.

■ **parget**

plaster, whitewash, or roughcast for coating a wall. Plaster work especially in raised ornamental figures on walls.

■ **pargeting**

the process of applying a plaster (as ornamental or waterproofing) or cement mortar coat to substrate such as masonry.

■ **parging**

the process of applying a coat of cement mortar to masonry.

■ **parking apron**

a paved or unpaved airfield surface used for fixed wing aircraft parking. The area includes parking lanes, taxi lanes, exits, and entrances. Aircraft move under their own power to the parking spaces, where they may be parked and secured with tiedowns. Parking designed to distribute aircraft for the purpose of increased survivability (dispersed hardstands) are included in this category code. For inventory purposes, only the prepared surface is included.

■ **partial differential equation**

a differential equation, which expresses the response of a system in terms of more than independent variables, it therefore contains partial derivatives.

■ **particulate matter**

solid material that escapes from combustion processes (fires).

■ **parting stop or strip**

a small wood piece used in the side and head jambs of double-hung windows to separate upper and lower sash.

■ **partition**

1. a wall that subdivides spaces within any story of a building.
2. interior dividing wall, one story or less in height.

Partition

■ **parts per million (ppm)**

the number of parts by weight of a substance per million parts of water. This unit is commonly used to represent pollutant concentrations. Large concentrations are expressed in percentages.

■ **Pascal's law**

a law of physics expressing conservation of momentum. It states that a pressure (force) applied to a confined fluid is transmitted equally in all directions through the fluid.

■ **pass**

the motion of a spray gun or roller in one direction only.

■ **passage**

a machined or cored fluid connection or path within a hydraulic component, which acts as a conductor of the fluid.

■ **passivate**

to make a surface such as steel inert, usually by chemical or electrochemical means.

■ **passivator**

a type of additive preventing corrosion and the catalytic effect of metals on oxidation.

■ **passive cooling**

the building's structure is designed to permit increased ventilation and retention of coolness within the building components. The intention is to minimise or eliminate the need for mechanical means of cooling.

■ **passive design**

building design and placement that allows the use of natural processes such as radiation, convection, absorption, and conduction to minimise energy costs.

■ **passive heating**

the building's structure is designed to allow natural thermal energy flows such as radiation, conduction, and natural convection generated by the sun to provide heat.

■ **passive solar water heater**

a water heating system that does not require mechanical pumps or controls to create hot water for domestic use. there are several types available commercially.

■ **paste**

the semi-fluid product of a dispersion process a: in coatings it is usually high in viscosity and may require dilution prior to application; a concentrated pigment dispersion used for shading lime putty caulking putty.

■ **pattern**

the shape or stream of material coming from a spray gun.

■ **pave**

inflected form(s)

■ **pavement**

the portion of the road, excluding shoulders, placed above the design sub grade level for the support of, and to form a running surface for, vehicular traffic.

■ **pavement distress**

the deterioration of the pavement evidenced by visible surface defects.

■ **pavement, paved**

asphalt or concrete that forms a firm level surface for parking, taxiing; to facilitate development

■ **paver**

a machine used to spread asphalt (or crushed rock) to uniform thickness and a level surface.

■ **paver stones**

usually pre-cast concrete slabs used to create a traffic surface.

■ **Pb**

lead. A heavy metal.

■ **PC**

point of curvature of a horizontal curve.

■ **PCB**

polychlorinated biphenyls. A toxic material.

■ **pearlite**

a two-phase microstructure found in some steels and cast irons. It results from the transformation of austenite of eutectoid compositions and consists of alternating layers of alpha-ferrite and cementite.

■ **pedestal**

a concrete or built-up metal member constructed on top of a bridge seat or pier for the purpose of providing a bearing seat at a specific elevation.

■ **peeling**

a film of paint or coating lifting from the surface due to poor adhesion or to moisture that travels through or on the substrate and accumulates under the paint where it expands when the temperature rises.

■ **pendentive**

a triangular shape that adapts the circular ring of a dome to fit onto a flat supporting wall.

■ **penetration**

1. any object passing through the roof.
2. the consistency (hardness) of a bituminous material expressed as the distance, in tenths of a millimetre (0.1 mm), that a standard needle penetrates vertically into a sample of material under specified conditions of loading, time, and temperature.

■ **penny**

as applied to nails, it originally indicated the price per hundred. The term now series as a measure of nail length and is abbreviated by the letter d.

■ **penstock**

a gate or sluice used in controlling the flow of water. A tube or trough for carrying water to a water wheel, or a pipe carrying water to an electric turbine.

■ **penthouse**

a relatively small structure built above the plane of the roof.

■ **percolating waters**

waters, which pass through the ground beneath the earth's surface without a definite channel. It is presumed that ground waters percolate.

■ **percolation**

the movement of water through the subsurface soil layers, usually continuing downward to the ground water or water table reservoirs.

■ **perforation of wells**

holes in the casing of wells, which allow water to flow into the well.

■ **performance**

the execution of an action; something accomplished; the fulfilment of a claim, promise, or request.

■ **perimeter**

the distance around the outside of a shape.

■ **perlite**

an aggregate used in lightweight insulating concrete and in preformed perlitic insulation boards, formed by heating and expanding siliceous volcanic glass.

■ **perm**

a measure of water vapour movement through a material (grains per square foot per hour per inch of mercury difference in vapour pressure).

■ **permafrost**

the part of the earth's surface that is permanently frozen.

■ **permeability**

capable of being permeated. Having pores or openings that permit liquids or gases to pass through. The degree to which a membrane or coating film (including paint and damp-proofing) will allow the passage or penetration of a liquid or gas.

■ **permittivity**

the proportionality constant between the dielectric displacement D and the electric field E.

■ **perspire**

to produce sweat or salty water from glands in the skin. A natural way of cooling the body by the evaporation of water.

■ **pervious paving**

paving material that allows water to penetrate to the soil below.

■ **petrochemicals**

chemical substances produced from petroleum in refinery operations and as fuel oil residues. These include fluoranthene, chrysene, mineral spirits, and refined oils. Petrochemicals are the bases from, which volatile organic compounds (VOCs), plastics, and many pesticides are made. These chemical substances are often toxic to humans and the environment.

■ **pH**

a way of expressing both acidity and alkalinity on a scale of 0:14, with 7 representing neutrality; numbers less than 7 indicate increasing acidity and numbers greater than 7 indicate increasing alkalinity.

■ **phase**

a homogeneous region of matter.

■ **phase construction**

in roofing the practice of applying the felt plies of the built-up roofing membrane in two or more operations, separated by a delay of at least one day.

■ **phase diagram**

a graphical representation of the relationships between environmental constraints, composition, and regions of phase stability, ordinarily under conditions of equilibrium.

■ **phase lag-time lag**

the angle by which the cycling output lags behind a sinusoidal input. Sometimes it is simply called 'phase.'

■ **phase margin**

the additional phase angle in degrees required to lag the input to cause 180° phase lag in output.

■ **phase transformation**

a change in the number and/or character of the phases that constitute the microstructure of an alloy.

■ **phased application**

the installation of separate roof system or waterproofing system component(s) during two or more separate time intervals. Application of surfacings at different time intervals are typically not considered phased application. (see **surfacing**.)

■ **phenolic**

a synthetic resin used for heat or water resistance.

■ **phonon-**

a single quantum of vibrational or elastic energy.

■ **phosphatising**

steel pre-treatment by a chemical solution containing phosphates and phosphoric acid to (temporarily) inhibit corrosion.

■ **photon**

a quantum unit of electromagnetic energy.

■ **photo-oxidation**

oxidation caused by rays of the sun.

■ **photosynthesis**

a process in green plants in which water, carbon dioxide, and sunlight combine to form sugar.

■ **photovoltaic**

the process of converting sunlight directly into electricity. The electricity can be used immediately, stored in batteries, or sold to a utility. Costs continue to drop and efficiency is improving for this technology.

■ **phreatophytes**

plants that send their roots into or below the capillary fringe to use ground water.

■ **physical stability**

the resistance possessed by a fluid to physical changes promoted by state conditions (pressure and temperature), contamination, and mechanical shear.

■ **physical-chemical treatment processes**

a means of wastewater treatment using both physical and chemical processes.

■ **pi**

point of intersection of a horizontal curve

■ **pick and dip**

a method of laying brick whereby the bricklayer simultaneously picks up a brick with one hand and, with the other hand, enough mortar on a trowel to lay the brick. Sometimes called the New England or eastern method.

■ **pickling**

steel pre-treatment for the removal of rust and mill scale by immersion in a hot acid solution containing an inhibitor.

■ **picture framing**

a square or rectangular pattern of buckles or ridges in a roof covering generally coinciding with insulation or deck joints; generally, a function of movement of the substrate.

■ **PID controller**

a device that utilises the Proportional-Integral-Derivative algorithm to accomplish its control goal.

■ **pier**

1. a column of masonry, usually rectangular in horizontal cross section, used to support other structural members.
2. a vertical supporting structure, such as a pillar.

■ **pier cap**

horizontal surface of a pier upon which rests the pedestals and/or bearings. All piers have a pier cap.

■ **pier stem**

the main body of a solid pier that extends from the top of the footing and supports the pedestals.

■ **piezoelectric**

a dielectric material in which polarisation is induced by the application of external forces.

■ **pigment**

finely ground natural or synthetic, insoluble fine powder adding colour and/or opacity or corrosion inhibition to a coating film.

■ **pigment / binder ratio**

ratio of total pigment to binder solids in paint.

■ **pigment grind**

the action of dispersing pigment in the liquid vehicle.

■ **pigment volume concentration (PVC)**

the percent by volume occupied by pigment in the dried film of paint.

■ **pilaster**

upright member that is rectangular in plan and is structurally a pier but architecturally treated as a column and that usually projects less than a third of its width from the base wall. This projection can occur from either or both wall faces.

■ **pile**

a long, relatively slender structural foundation element, usually made of timber, steel or reinforced or prestressed concrete, driven or jetted in the ground or cast in place in a borehole; the purpose is to support vertical or lateral loads, to form a wall to exclude or resist water or soft material or to compact the surrounding ground.

■ **pile driver**

a noisy machine that repeatedly drops a heavy weight on top of a pile until the pile reaches solid soil or rock or cannot be pushed down any farther.

■ **pile shoe**

reinforcing steel plates attached to the tips of piles to prevent excessive damage during driving. Used where hard driving conditions are expected.

■ **pillar**

post; firm upright support for a superstructure. A usually ornamental column or shaft; especially : one standing alone for a monument. Solid mass of rock, coal, or ore left standing to support a tunnel or mine roof rock. Body part that resembles a column rock.

■ **pilot control**

a method of operating valves and other devices by means of a small independent pressure signal.

■ **pilot pressure**

a pressure used to actuate or control hydraulic components.

■ **pilot valve**

a small valve used to control the operation of larger valves.

■ **pinholing**

film defect characterised by small, pore-like flaws in a coating which extend entirely through the film.

■ **pipe boot**

prefabricated flashing piece used to flash around circular pipe penetrations.

■ **piston**

a cylindrical member forming the internal element of a cylinder assembly and transmits or receives motion by means of a connecting rod. It is the component within a cylinder on, which fluid acts to convert pressure energy into linear motion.

■ **piston motor/pump**

a rotary actuator or pump, which employs pistons to transmit hydraulic or shaft power.

■ **pitch**

the incline slope of a roof or the ratio of the total rise to the total width of a house, i.e., an 8-foot rise and 24-foot width is a one-third pitch roof. Roof-slope is expressed in the inches of rise per foot of run.

■ **pitch pan or pocket**

a bottomless metal box placed on the burm around irregular projections. These are subsequently filled with coal tar pitch or mastic to effect a weather tight seal.

■ **pitch pocket**

an opening extending parallel to the annual rings of growth, that usually contains, or has contained, either solid or liquid pitch.

■ **pitch-pocket (pitch-pan)**

a flanged, open bottomed enclosure made of sheet metal or other material, placed around a penetration through the roof, filled with grout and bituminous or polymeric sealants to seal the area around the penetration.

■ **pith**

the small, soft core at the original centre of a tree around which wood formation takes place.

■ **place of use**

the specific location where water is applied or used. A water user cannot use water at another location without transferring the right or obtaining a new right.

■ **Planck's constant**

a universal constant that has a value of 6.63 x 10^{-34} J.

■ **plaster grounds**

strips of wood used as guides or strike off edges around window and door openings and at base of walls.

■ **plastic**

a solid material in the primary ingredient of which is an organic polymer of high molecular weight.

■ **plastic blow moulding die**

a piece of precision-made mass production tooling used to blow mould plastic bottles, watering cans and other plastic containers.

■ **plastic cement**

a roofing industry generic term used to describe Type I asphalt roof cement that is a trowel-able mixture of solvent-based bitumen, mineral stabilisers, other fibres and/or fillers. Generally, intended for use on relatively low slopes — not vertical surfaces.

■ **plastic deformation**

displacements that occur outside the elastic range of the member, where the member does not return to its original undeformed shape when the load is removed.

■ **plastic extrusion die**

a piece of precision-made mass production tooling used to extrude long continuous plastic shapes of uniform cross section such as tubing / hose, guttering, rigid pipe, refrigerator door seals, plastic coated wire, weatherboards, plastic food wrap, and plastic carry bags.

■ **plastic injection mould/die**

a piece of precision-made mass production tooling used to injection mould molten plastic into shape. Injection moulded components include gears, hearing aid cases, combs & hair clips, plastic bottle caps, syringes, car tail light lenses, domestic appliance components (such as hair-dryer, vacuum cleaner, and swimming pool filter bodies and components), computer keyboards, food storage containers (for example, Tupperware), children's toys, washing baskets, outdoor furniture, and wheelie bins.

■ **plasticiser**

a chemical added materials such as mortars, rubbers and coating resins to impart flexibility, workability, or stretch ability.

■ **plate**

1. sill plate: a horizontal member anchored to a masonry wall.
2. sole plate: bottom horizontal member of a frame wall.
3. top plate: top horizontal member of a frame wall supporting ceiling joists, rafters, or other members.

■ **plate girder**

a girder that is built up of individual steel plates.

■ **playas**

the flat floored bottom of an undrained desert basin, which may become a shallow lake.

■ **piezometric surface**

an imaginary surface, which coincides with the hydrostatic pressure level of the water in an aquifer.

■ **plinth**

a solid mass of concrete that surrounds a pier to protect it from water and ice flows.

■ **plough**

to cut a lengthwise groove in a board or plank.

■ **plumb**

exactly perpendicular; vertical.

■ **plumb rule**

this is a combination plumb rule and level. It is used in a horizontal position as a level and in a vertical position as a plumb rule. They are made in lengths of 42 and 48 inches, and short lengths from 12 to 24 inches.

■ **plume**

a visible or measurable discharge of a contaminant from a given point of origin. It can be visible or thermal in water or visible in the air, such as a plume of smoke.

■ **plunger pump**

this pump operates practically the same as a piston pump. The primary difference is that the plunger moves through a stationary packed seal; whereas a piston pump seal is carried on the piston itself (e.g., piston rings). Plunger pumps are by necessity, single acting. Both piston and plunger pumps are self-priming.

■ **ply**

a term to denote the number of thickness or layers of roofing felt, veneer in plywood, or layers in built-up materials, in any finished piece of such material.

■ **plywood**

1. wooden panels formed by gluing thin sheets of wood together, with the grain of adjacent layers arranged at right angles.
2. a piece of wood made of three or more layers of veneer joined with glue, and usually laid with the grain of adjoining plies at right angles. Almost always an odd number of plies are used to provide balanced construction.

■ **pneumatics**

if energy transfer is in the form of compressed airflow then it is known as pneumatics. In industry compressed air is generated by using a machine called a compressor,, which draws in normal air, squeezes it to increase its pressure and then passes it through a moisture separator and stores it in the reservoir for later use in the factory.

■ **PO$_4$**

phosphate. A nutrient.

■ **point defect**

a crystalline defect associated with one or, at most, several atomic sites.

■ **point of diversion**

the point from, which water is diverted from a source.

■ **point source**

a stationary source of a large individual air pollution emission, generally of an industrial nature.

■ **point source pollution**

this type of water pollution results from the discharges into receiving waters from easily identifiable points. Common point sources of pollution are discharges from factories and municipal sewage treatment plants.

■ **pointing**

1. finishing a mortar joint after the masonry units are laid.
2. the process where joints between masonry units, brick, etc., are filled with mortar.

■ **Poiseuille law**

states that the quantity of fluid that flows through a small tube in a given time is proportional to the pressure difference and to the fourth power of the internal diameter of the tube, and varies inversely with its length.

■ **Poisson's ratio**

for elastic deformation, the negative ratio of lateral and axial strains that result from an applied axial stress.

■ **polar molecule**

a molecule in which there exists a permanent electric dipole moment by virtue of the asymmetrical distribution of positively and negatively charged regions.

■ **polar substances**

molecules in, which a permanent separation of positive and negative charges exist; thus conferring a dipole moment to the molecule.

■ **polarisation (electronic)**

for an atom, the displacement of the centre of the negatively charged electron cloud relative to the positive nucleus, which is induced by an electric field.

■ **polarisation (ionic)**

polarisation as a result of the displacement of anions and cations in opposite directions.

■ **polarisation (orientation)**

polarisation resulting from the alignment (by rotation) of permanent electric dipole moments with an applied electric field.

■ **polished aggregate friction value (PAFV)**

a measure, on a scale of 0 to 100, of the resistance of an aggregate to polishing under the action of traffic as determined in standard laboratory tests.

■ **polished stone value (PSV)**

a measure, similar to PAFV, but based on a British standard.

■ **polluted**

something, which contains foreign substances.

■ **pollution**

the alteration of the physical, thermal, chemical or biological quality of, or the contamination of, any water in the state that renders the water harmful, detrimental, or injurious to humans, animal life, vegetation, or property or to public health, safety, or welfare, or impairs the usefulness or the public enjoyment of the water for any lawful or reasonable purpose.

■ **polychlorinated biphenyls (PCBS)**

a group of toxic chemicals used for a variety of purposes including electrical applications, carbonless copy paper, adhesives, hydraulic fluids, microscope emersion oils, and caulking compounds. PCBs are also produced in certain combustion processes. PCBs are extremely persistent in the environment because they are very stable, non— reactive, and highly heat resistant. Chronic exposure to PCBs is believed to cause liver damage. It is also known to bioaccumulate in fatty tissues.

■ **polycrystalline**

referring to crystalline materials that are composed of more than one crystal or grain.

■ **polycyclic aromatic hydrocarbons or polararomatic hydrocarcons (PAHS)**

PAHs, such as pyrene, are groups of highly reactive organic compounds. They are a component of creosotes and can cause cancer.

■ **polyester**

a polymeric resin which is generally cross-linked or cured and made into a variety of plastic materials and products. Polyester fibres are widely used as the reinforcing medium in reinforced membranes. (See polyester fibre.)

■ **polyester fibre**

a synthetic fibre usually formed by extrusion. Scrims made of polyester fibre are used for fabric reinforcement.

■ **polyester resin**

group of synthetic resins which contain repeating ester groups. A special type of modified alkyd resin.

■ **polymer**

1. substance of molecules, which consist of one or more structural units repeated any number of times.
2. a substance consisting of large molecules, which have been formed from smaller molecules of similar make-up.

■ **polymer modified bitumen (PMB)**

a binder consisting of polymeric materials dispersed in bitumen with enhanced binder performance for particular applications.

■ **polymerisation**

chemical reaction in which two or more small molecules combine to form large molecules containing repeated structural units.

■ **polymorphism**

the ability of a solid material to exist in more than one form or crystal structure.

■ **polynuclear aromatic hydrocarbons(PNAs)**

PNAs, such as naphthalene, and biphenyls, are a group of highly reactive organic compounds that are a common component of creosotes, which can be carcinogenic.

■ **polytropic process**

an expansion or compression of a gas in, which the quantity PVn is held constant, where P and V are the pressure and volume of the gas, and n is a constant.

■ **polyurethane**

group of thermoplastic or thermosetting polymers containing polyisocyanate; they may be hard and glossy forms; drawn into fibres; elastomeric or rubbery and flexible, or rigid foams. Used as rubber, for coatings, as fibres and foams; also used complexed in other polymers.

■ **polyvinyl chloride (PVC)**

a synthetic thermoplastic polymer prepared from vinylchloride. PVC can be com-pounded into flexible and rigid forms through the use of plasticisers, stabilisers, fillers, and other modifiers; rigid forms are used in pipes; flexible forms are used in the manufacture of sheeting and roof membrane materials.

■ **ponding**

a condition where water stands on a roof for prolonged periods due to poor drainage and/or deflection of the deck.

■ **pop rivets**

fasteners used to join pieces of metal that are installed by either compressed air assisted or hand operated guns. Unique in that they are installed from one side of the work.

■ **poppet**

A valve element, which prevents flow when it closes against a conical shaped seat.

■ **poppet valve**

a valve, which prevents flow when the valve element (poppet) closes against a conical shaped seat and opens when the element is lifted from the seat.

■ **pore space**

that portion of rock or soil not occupied by solid mineral matter and, which may be occupied by ground water.

■ **pores**

wood cells of comparatively large diameter that have open ends and are set one above the other to form continuous tubes. The openings of the vessels on the surface of a piece of wood are referred to as pores.

■ **porosity**

the presence of numerous minute voids in a material; condition(of a solid substance) of having pores or open spaces. The density of substance and its capacity to pass liquids.

■ **porous**

a condition, which allows liquids to pass through.

■ **port**

an opening at a surface of a component; e.g., the internal or external terminus of a passage in a component.

■ **portland cement**

a hydraulic cement made by finely pulverising the clinker produced by calcining to incipient fusion a mixture of clay and limestone or similar materials.

■ **positive displacement**

a characteristic of a particular pump or motor, which has the inlet positively sealed from the outlet so that fluid cannot recirculate in the component.

■ **positive drainage**

the drainage condition in which consideration has been made during design for all loading deflections of the deck, and additional roof slope has been provided to ensure drainage of the roof area within 48 hours of rainfall, during ambient drying conditions.

■ **positive position stop**

a structural member, which rigidly limits the working motion at a desired position.

■ **post**

piece (as of timber or metal) fixed firmly in an upright position especially as a stay or support.

■ **post-tensioned member**

a concrete member where the prestressing force is applied after the concrete has cured.

■ **pot life**

the length of time a paint material is useful after its original package is opened or a catalyst or other curing agent is added.

■ **potable water**

water fit for human consumption; drinking water.

■ **potential**

a water quality issue or problem identified by a river authority as being a potential problem, or a problem without current supporting data.

■ **pothole**

a hole eroded in the solid rock of a stream bed by water carried sand and pebbles.

■ **pour coat**

the top coating of bitumen on a built-up roof.

■ **pourable sealer**

a type of sealant often supplied in two parts, and used at difficult-to-flash penetrations, typically in conjunction with pitch-pockets to form a seal.

■ **powder pillow**

small, plastic containers with premeasured amounts of chemicals; easily opened with nail clippers.

■ **power**

the time rate of doing work or the work done per unit time. Measured in horsepower or watts.

■ **power pack**

a unit which usually includes a fluid reservoir, prime mover, a pump, and essential control valves.

■ **ppm**

the parts per million concentration; e.g., mg/kg or ml/m³.

■ **practical coverage**

the spreading rate of a paint/coating calculated at the recommended dry film thickness and assuming 15 per cent material loss.

■ **precast**

concrete member that is cast and cured at a fabrication facility as opposed to its final position. The member must be transported and placed in the field.

■ **pre-charge**

the residual pressure in a hydraulic accumulator before the introduction of oil.

■ **precipitate(floc)**

material which is insoluble in water and will settle out over time.

■ **precipitation**

a deposit on the earth of hail, rain, mist, sleet, or snow. It is the common process by, which atmospheric water becomes surface or subsurface water. The term precipitation is also commonly used to designate the quantity of water precipitated.

■ **precipitation gauge**

a device used to collect precipitation and measure precipitation.

■ **precipitation hardening**

hardening and strengthening of a metal alloy by extremely small and uniformly dispersed particles that precipitate from a supersaturated solid solution.

■ **precoating**

the coating of aggregate with a liquid to improve adhesion with the bituminous binder and the aggregate.

■ **precursor**

something that precedes and indicates the approach of another. A condition from, which another condition is formed. A forerunner or warning of events that will occur.

■ **prefabricated brick masonry**

masonry construction fabricated somewhere other than its final in-service location in the structure. Also known as pre-assembled, panellised and sectionalised brick masonry.

■ **prefill valve**

an unusually large capacity two-way or pilot-check valve that is located between an overhead reservoir and the top of the working cylinder or ram of a hydraulic press. This valve allows a press ram to drop due to gravity without cavitation and draw in oil to fill the press ram.

■ **premix**

refer **cold mix**.

■ **prepreg**

continuous fibre reinforcement pre-impregnated with a polymer resin, which is then partially cured.

■ **preservative**

any substance that, for a reasonable length of time, will prevent the action of wood-destroying fungi, borers of various kinds, and similar destructive agents when the wood has been properly coated or impregnated with it.

■ **press tool (metal stamping die**

a piece of precision-made mass production tooling used to cut, bend and shape metal components from flat, strip, coil or sheet material. The components produced could range in size from car roof panels, door skins or bonnets, to small clockwork gears in mechanical watches and timepieces.

■ **pressure**

a measure of potential energy expressed in force per unit of area. The force exerted per unit area on a body.

■ **pressure drop**

the difference in pressure between any two points in a circuit. It represents the loss of energy of a pressure oil flow through a hydraulic element as a result of friction and conversion into heat.

■ **pressure fuse**

see **hydraulic fuse**.

■ **pressure gain**

the rate of change of load pressure drop with an increase in input signal at zero control flow (control ports blocked). It is usually specified as the average slope of the curve of load pressure drop vs. input signal between ± 40% of maximum load pressure drop.

■ **pressure line**

the conduit, which transmits fluid under pressure.

■ **pressure override**

the difference between the cracking pressure of a valve and the pressure reached when the valve is passing full flow.

■ **pressure plate**

a side plate in a gear or vane pump or motor cartridge to minimise the clearance and slippage.

■ **pressure reducing valve**

a pressure control valve whose primary function is to limit the outlet pressure.

■ **pressure switch**

an electric switch operated by fluid pressure and responsive to a rise or drop in pressure.

■ **pressure, absolute**

the sum of atmospheric and gauge pressure.

■ **pressure, atmospheric**

the pressure at any point in the atmosphere due solely to the weight of the atmospheric gases above the point. Used synonymously with barometric pressure.

■ **pressure, back**

the pressure encountered on the return side of a system; e.g., reservoir pressure.

■ **pressure, barometric**

see **atmospheric pressure**.

■ **pressure, burst**

the pressure, which causes component rupture.

■ **pressure, charge**

the pressure at, which replenishing fluid is forced into a fluid power system.

■ **pressure, compensated**

describes a pump or control valve whose output is automatically regulated in response to variations in system pressure.

■ **pressure, operating**

the pressure at, which the system is operated.

■ **pressure, peak**

the highest pressure noted in a hydraulic system.

■ **pressure, precharge**

the pressure of compressed gas in an accumulator prior to the admission of liquid.

■ **pressure, proof**

the non-destructive test pressure in excess of the maximum rated operating pressure.

■ **pressure, rated**

the maximum qualified operating pressure, which is recommended for a component or system by the manufacturer.

■ **pressure, relief valve**

a pressure control valve, which by-passes pump delivery and thus limits circuit or system pressure to a predetermined maximum value.

■ **pressure, snubber**

a pressure snubber protects sensitive components against pulsating or surge pressures. Damping is accomplished by porous metal devices or a small restricting orifice upstream of the gauge. These snubbers are sometimes called a 'gauge savers'.

■ **pressure, static**

the pressure existing in a fluid at rest.

■ **pressure, suction**

the pressure at the suction port of the pump.

■ **pressure, surge**

the pressure existing due to surge conditions.

■ **pressure, vapour**

the pressure, at a given fluid temperature, in, which the liquid and gaseous phases are in equilibrium.

■ **pressure, working**

the pressure, which overcomes the resistance of the working device load and line loses.

■ **pressure-treated wood**

wood that is chemically preserved to prevent moisture decay. The process uses environmentally dangerous chemicals and there can be health hazards form working with, or coming into contact with, the material. If pressure treated wood is required for a residential application, CCA preserved wood is the better choice at this time. Follow all safety procedures when using this type of material.

■ **pressurised water reactor**

a reactor in, which water, heated by nuclear energy, is kept at high pressure to prevent the water from boiling. Steam is then generated in a secondary coolant loop.

■ **prestressed member**

a concrete member that has a pre-applied compressive force in the areas that will experience tension in service.

■ **pretensioned**

prestressing process where the prestressing tendons are stressed before the concrete is placed.

■ **primary bond**

interatomic bonds that are relatively strong and for which bonding energies are relatively large.

■ **primary treatment**

process that removes the largest solid material and many microorganisms from wastewater, before it enters holding ponds for further purification. Primer first coat of paint/coating applied to a surface, formulated to have good bonding, wetting and inhibiting properties.

■ **prime**

an application of a primer to a prepared base, without cover aggregate, to provide penetration of the surface, temporary waterproofing and to obtain a bond between the pavement and the subsequent seal or asphalt. It is a preliminary treatment to a more permanent bituminous surfacing.

■ **primer**

1. the first coat of paint in a paint job that consists of two or more coats; also the paint used for such a first coat. A bituminous material of low viscosity and low surface tension used in priming.
2. a material of relatively thin consistency applied to a surface for the purpose of creating a more secure bonding surface.

■ **primer binder**

a material more viscous than a primer and required to act both as a primer and binder, and used in primer sealing.

■ **primer seal**

an application of a primer binder with a fine cover aggregate to a prepared base to provide penetration of the surface and retain a light cover of aggregate. It is used as a preliminary treatment to a more permanent bituminous surfacing. It is intended to carry traffic for a longer period than a prime.

■ **priority valve**

used when one particular circuit must always have priority over all other circuits for flow, irrespective of other demands.

■ **prism**

small masonry assemblage made with masonry units and mortar. Primarily used to predict the compressive and flexural strengths of full scale masonry members.

■ **probability**

a mathematical estimate of the possible realisation of a random event or random quantity.

■ **production jigs and fixtures**

precision-made mass production tooling used to safely and accurately position and hold components during a production line process, to allow follow-on operations such as machining, welding, painting, assembly and/or packaging to be undertaken on the component.

■ **profile**

1. the term used to describe the anchor pattern of a surface produced by sandblasting, acid etching or similar method.

2. refers to shape of the road in cross section.

■ **programmable thermostat**

a mechanical or electronic device that regulates the temperature setting and time of day operation of heating and cooling systems. the temperature and time of day settings are determined by the user so that optimal efficiency can be attained while maintaining comfort levels as needed.

■ **projection**

any object or equipment which pierces the roof membrane.

■ **proper ventilation**

combustion gases are vented completely to the outdoors. Combustion gases that escape into a living space can pose health hazards such as lung cancer.

■ **proportional**

a relationship one variable to another for which there is a constant ratio.

■ **proportional control**

a control action producing a controller output proportional to the size of the deviation.

■ **proportional control valve**

a control valve whose output is directly proportional to the input signal.

■ **proportional limit**

the point on a stress-strain curve at which the straight line proportionality between stress and strain ceases.

■ **protected membrane roof**

an insulated and ballasted roofing assembly, in which the insulation and ballast are applied on top of the membrane (sometimes referred to as an 'inverted roof assembly').

■ **protection board**

heavy asphalt impregnated boards which are laid over bituminous coatings to protect against mechanical injury.

■ **PS&E**

plans, specifications and estimate - the final submittal from the designer that contains all necessary contract drawings, special specifications and the final engineers estimate.

■ **PT**

point of tangency of a horizontal curve.

■ **p-type semiconductor**

a semiconductor for which the predominant charge carriers responsible for electrical conduction are holes. Normally, acceptor impurity atoms give rise to the excess holes.

■ **puddle**

a small pool of water, usually a few inches in depth and from several inches to several feet in its greatest dimension.

■ **pugmill**

a device for mixing aggregate, sand and binder.

■ **pump**

a device, which converts mechanical torque and motion into hydrau-

lic power (flow and pressure). Also known as a 'hydraulic generator' and used to transport energy-laden fluid to the actuators.

■ **pump, booster**

a pump used to boost the fluid entering the suction port of a hydraulic pump.

■ **pumped hydroelectric storage**

storing water for future use in generating electricity. Excess electrical energy produced during a period of low demand is used to pump water up to a reservoir. When demand is high, the water is released to operate a hydroelectric generator.

■ **puncture resistance**

extent to which a material is able to withstand the action of a sharp object without perforation.

■ **purlin**

horizontal secondary structural member that transfers loads from the primary structural framing.

■ **putty**

a type of cement usually made of whiting and boiled linseed oil, beaten or kneaded to the consistency of dough, and used in sealing glass in sash, filling small holes and crevices in wood, and for similar purposes.

■ **PVC**

point of vertical curvature

■ **PVI**

point of vertical intersection

■ PVT

point of vertical tangency

■ pyroclastic flows

high-density fluid mixtures of hot, dry rock fragments and hot gases that move away from their source (volcanic vents) at high speeds. They may result from the explosive eruption of molten or solid rock fragments, or both, or from the collapse of vertical eruption columns of ash and larger rock fragments.

■ pyrometer

instrument used to measure surface temperatures.

■ quadratic

another name for second order, based on the form of the equation, which represents the second order response.

■ quadro riportato

the simulation of a wall painting for a ceiling design in which painted scenes are arranged in panels resembling frames on the surface of a shallow, curved vault.

■ quadrupole spectrometer

an instrument allowing ions to pass along a line of symmetry between four parallel cylindrical rods, that filters out all ions except those with a predetermined mass.

■ qualification

the entire process by which products of manufacturers and distributors are examined and tested and then identified on a list of qualified products (qpl).

■ quality

an inherent or distinguishing characteristic of a material, product or assembly. Or, having a high degree of excellence. The quality of a thing tends to be better the more care, thought (and often money) its maker puts into its making.

■ quality assurance

techniques and systems ensuring that a high (or at least a predetermined) level of quality is maintained through various stages of a process at the owner, rather than at the provider, end of the business.

■ quality control

techniques and systems ensuring that a high (or at least a predetermined) level of quality is maintained through various stages of a process at the provider rather than at the owner end of the business.

■ quality of life

the degree of emotional, intellectual, or visual/cultural satisfaction in a person's everyday life as distinct from the degree of material comfort.

■ quarry

an open pit mine from which stone is taken by cutting, digging or blasting.

■ **quarry fines**

terms used in quarry and sand products.

■ **quarter round**

a small moulding that has the cross section of a quarter circle.

■ **quatrefoil**

in architecture, an ornament having four leaves, lobes, or foils.

■ **queen closure (closer)**

cut brick having a nominal 2 in. Horizontal face dimension; half brick used in a masonry course to prevent vertical joints from falling one above another.

■ **quick disconnect**

a coupling usually containing at least one check valve, which can be rapidly disconnected with minimal leakage.

■ **quick test**

a shear test of a cohesive soil without allowing the sample to drain.

■ **quicklime**

lime, burnt lime, caustic lime.

■ **quoin**

1. projecting right angle masonry corner.

2. corner stones lending either strength or emphasis, distinguished from the rest of the surface by greater size, different colour, rustication, or the imitation of same in brick or paint; b: a large square ashlar or stone at the angle of a wall to limit the rubble and make the corner true and strong; an exterior masonry corner.
3. the keystone of an arch.
4. a wedge to support or steady a stone.

■ **quoin header**

corner header in the face wall which also serves as a stretcher for the side wall; a large, sometimes rusticated, usually slightly projecting stone (or stones) that often form the corners of the exterior walls of masonry buildings.

■ **quoin post**

heel post.

■ **quoins**

large squared stones such as buttresses.

■ **quv**

an accelerated testing device designed to evaluate the aging and colour fading properties of a coating by exposure to high intensity, ultraviolet light.

■ **rabbet**

a rectangular longitudinal groove cut in the corner edge of a board or plank.

■ **rabbet mount**

a mounting configuration, which utilises matching male and female forms (usually coaxial circular) between the cylinder and its mating mounting element.

■ **racking**

a method entailing stepping back successive courses of masonry.

■ **RAD**

the unit of energy absorbed by a material from ionising radiation. One RAD is equal to $(1.0\ e + 12)$ joules per kilogram (100 ergs per gram).

■ **radial draw forming**

forming metals by the simultaneous application of tangential stretch and radial compression forces.

■ **radiant barrier**

a layer of metallic foil that reflects thermal radiation without transferring heat to other materials.

■ **radiant heating**

a method of heating, usually consisting of a forced hot water system with pipes placed in the floor, wall, or ceiling; or with electrically heated panels.

■ **radon**

a radioactive, colourless, odourless gas that occurs naturally in the earth. When trapped in buildings, concentrations build up, and it can cause health hazards such as lung cancer.

■ **rafter**

one of a series of structural members of a roof designed to support roof loads. The rafters of a flat roof are sometimes called roof joists.

■ **rafter, hip**

a rafter that forms the intersection of an external roof angle.

■ **rafter, valley**

a rafter that forms the intersection of an internal roof angle. The valley rafter is normally made of double 2-inch-thick members.

■ **raggle**

a groove in a joint or special unit to receive roofing or flashing.

■ **raggle block**

a specially designed masonry block having a slot or opening into which the top edge of the roof flashing is inserted and anchored.

■ **rail**

cross members of panel doors or of a sash. Also the upper and lower members of a balustrade or staircase extending from one vertical support, such as a post, to another.

■ **rain**

water drops, which fall to the earth from the air.

■ **rain gauge**

any instrument used for recording and measuring time, distribution, and the amount of rainfall.

■ **rain sensor**

a simple, inexpensive device that measures rainfall and prevents unnecessary irrigation with an automatic controller.

■ **rainfall**

the quantity of water that falls as rain only.

■ **rake**

trim members that run parallel to the roof slope and form the finish between the wall and a gable roof extension. The angle of slope of a roof rafter, or the inclined portion of a cornice.

■ **ram**

a single-acting cylinder in, which the movable element has approximately the same cross-sectional area as the cylinder bore. Hence, a ram has a single diameter type plunger as opposed to a piston and rod. The plunger in a ram-type cylinder is also called a ram.

■ **rammed earth**

a building technique for exterior walls where earth is "rammed" (or processed down) between forms. Certain mixtures of moistened earth used in this technique harden under pressure and form a strong solid wall, which is then covered by a waterproofing coat.

■ **ramp input function**

an inclined slope, a constantly increasing function, a linear intensification of magnitude.

■ **random copolymer**

a polymer in which two different mer units are randomly distributed along the molecular chain.

■ **ratchetting**

a stick-slip action (intermittent motion) of the control system.

■ **rated**

refers to the manufacturer's designation of the normal operating condition the maximum, allowable, continuous, etc.

■ **ratio of specific heats**

the ratio of the amount of heat required to raise a mass of material 1 degree in temperature to the amount of heat required to raise an equal mass of a reference substance 1 degree in temperature.

■ **ravelling**

the loosening of stones from the surface of a pavement.

■ **raw linseed oil**

the crude product processed from flaxseed and usually without much subsequent treatment.

■ **RBM**

reinforced brick masonry.

■ **reagent**

chemical added to a sample; may be in powder or liquid form.

■ **rebar**

(slang) reinforcing steel.

■ **recharge**

the addition of water into a ground water system.

■ **recharge, artificial**

the infusion of surface water into wells; seepage of water into soil or gravely areas for storage.

■ **reciprocation**

a back-and-forth straight-line motion or oscillation.

■ **reclamation**

the process of matter or energy being reclaimed or restored to a better or useful state. For instance, dams reclaim water, which would otherwise be lost through runoff.

■ **reconstitued**

the process of taking small pieces of material and binding them together to form a larger item. Examples include wood chips that are adhered together to form substrates and/or structural components in trim, doors, windows, structural material, and sheet materials. Finger jointed and laminated materials are other examples.

■ **recorder, stream data**

a mechanical apparatus, which records a continuous record of a water level.

■ **re-cover**

the addition of a new roof membrane or steep-slope roof covering over a major portion of an existing roof assembly. This process does not involve removal of the existing roofing.

■ **recrystallisation**

the formation of a new set of strain-free grains within a previously cold-worked material; normally an annealing heat treatment is necessary.

■ **recycled plastic lumber**

recycled plastic made into lumber, which is workable like lumber. There are several manufacturers of this material. It is insect and water resistant.

■ **recycling**

the reuse of paving material. Processes include hot and cold and can be in situ or off site.

■ **redundancy**

the existence of more than one means for accomplishing a given function.

■ **redundant**

a structure with multiple load paths so that, should a failure in a member occur, the structure would not collapse.

■ **reflection**

deflection of a light beam at the interface between two media.

■ **reflective**

a term referring to a material that has a white or shiny metallic surface.

■ **reflective insulation**

sheet material with one or both sun faces of comparatively low heat emissive, such as aluminium foil. When used in building construction the surfaces face air spaces, reducing the radiation across the air space.

■ **refraction**

bending of a light beam upon passing from one medium into another.

■ **refractive index**

the ratio of the velocity of light in a vacuum to the velocity of light in some medium.

■ **refractory**

a metal or ceramic that may be exposed to extremely high temperatures without deteriorating rapidly or without melting.

■ **regeneration**

the recovery of energy that would ordinarily be lost.

■ **regenerative control system**

a system where part or all of the output is fed back to help drive the function or is stored for driving the output converter.

■ **reglet**

a horizontal slot, formed or cut in a parapet or other masonry wall, into which the top edge of counter flashing can be inserted and anchored.

■ **regulating course**

an asphalt course of varying thickness applied to a pavement surface to adjust its shape preparatory to overlaying with another course or applying a sprayed seal.

■ **regulation**

the control of fluid energy with simultaneous feedback of fluctuations for comparison of input/actual values related to system or component.

■ **rehabilitation**

the process of returning a property to a state of utility, through repair or alteration, which makes possible an efficient contemporary use while preserving those portions and features of the property which are significant to its historic, architectural, and cultural values. Rehabilitation not only encourages the repair of historic buildings, it allows appropriate alterations to ensure their efficient contemporary use. Examples include the continued use of hotels, stores, and private residences, as well as the adaptation of vacant schools into apartments, warehouses into offices, and industrial buildings into commercial space. Because rehabilitation focuses on how buildings can be successfully used for contemporary purposes, it may be considered somewhat more flexible than more traditional treatments, such as preservation and restoration. But even though rehabilitation allows for more change, a historic building's distinctive materials, features, and spaces still must be preserved. Process of restoring a distressed pavement, e.g.. overlay, patching.

re-impregnate

to replace oils and bitumen in the components of the burm which through weathering and oxidation, have been lost.

reinforced concrete

concrete with steel bars or mesh embedded in it for increased strength in tension; in pre-tensioned concrete, the embedded steel bars or cables are stretched into tension before the concrete hardens; in post-tensioned concrete, the embedded steel bars or cables are stretched into tension after the concrete hardens.

reinforced masonry

masonry units, reinforcing steel, grout and/or mortar combined to act together in resisting forces.

reinforced membrane

a roofing or waterproofing membrane that has been strengthened by the addition or incorporation of one or more reinforcing materials, including woven or non-woven glass fibres, polyester mats or scrims, nylon, or polyethylene sheeting.

reinforcing

steel rods or metal fabric placed in concrete slabs, beams, or columns to increase their strength.

relative humidity

the amount of water vapour in the atmosphere, expressed as a percentage of the maximum quantity that could be present at a given temperature. (The actual amount of water vapour that can be held in space increases with the temperature.)

relative magnetic permeability

the ratio of the magnetic permeability of some medium to that of a vacuum.

reliability

the capability of a system to perform its intended design function for an acceptable period of time under a given set of operating conditions.

remedial design

an engineering phase that follows the remedial investigation/feasibility study and includes development of engineering drawings and specifications for a site cleanup.

remedial investigation

an in-depth study designed to gather the data necessary to determine the nature and extent of contamination at a Superfund site; establish criteria for cleaning up the site; identify preliminary alternatives for remedial actions; and support the technical and cost analyses of the alternatives. The remedial investigation is usually done with the feasibility study. Together they are usually referred to as the RI/PS.

remedial response

a long-term action that stops or substantially reduces a release or threatened release of hazardous substances that is serious, but does not pose an immediate threat to public health and/or the environment.

removal action

short-term immediate actions taken to address releases of hazardous substances that require expedited response.

repeatability

quantitative expression of the random error associated with a single tester in a given laboratory.

replacement

the practice of removing an existing roof system down to the roof deck and replacing it with a new roofing system.

replenish

to add fluid to maintain the volume of a hydraulic system makeup or top-out fluid.

reproducibility

quantitative expression of the random error, associated with testers working in different laboratories, each obtaining single results on identical test material, using same method. That is, the precision with, which the measurement of a given quantity can be duplicated in separate facilities.

reroofing

the process of re-covering, or tearing-off and replacing an existing roof system.

reseal

a seal over an existing bituminous surface.

reservoir

a pond, lake, tank, or basin (natural or human made) where water is collected and used for storage. Large bodies of ground water are called ground water reservoirs; water behind a dam is also called a reservoir of water.

reservoir, atmospheric

a reservoir that exposes the fluid media to atmospheric pressure, contains a vented opening.

reservoir, pressurised

a reservoir that is sealed to the atmosphere and maintains a pressure in the reservoir above atmospheric.

residual binder

a binder that remains in service after any volatiles have evaporated.

resilience

the ability of a seal or elastomeric material to return to its original shape after deformation.

resistivity

the reciprocal of electrical conductivity, and a measure of a material's resistance to the passage of electric current.

■ **resorcinol glue**

a glue that is high in both wet and dry strength and resistant to high temperatures. It is used for gluing lumber or assembly joints that must withstand severe service conditions.

■ **response time**

the time required for the system output to reach and stay within a specified percentage of its theoretical final value due to a step input – usually equal to five time constants.

■ **restore**

to put or bring back into existence or use. To bring back to or put back into a former or original state.

■ **restriction**

a reduced cross-sectional area in a line or passage, which produces a pressure drop.

■ **restrictor**

a device having a reduced fixed or variable area, which creates a deliberate pressure drop and resistance to the normal flow of fluid. Variable types are non-compensated, pressure-compensated, or pressure- and temperature-compensated.

■ **restrictor, choke**

a restrictor whose length is relatively large compared to its cross-sectional area.

■ **restrictor, orifice**

a restrictor, the length of, which is relatively small with respect to its cross-sectional area

■ **retrofit**

work done to an existing structure for the purpose of upgrading details that do not meet current standards.

■ **return**

any surface turned back from the face of a principal surface.

■ **return line**

a conduit used to carry the full pump flow being exhausted from actuators or bypass valves at low pressure back to the reservoir.

■ **reveal**

that portion of a jamb or recess which is visible from the face of a wall.

■ **Reynold's number**

the dimensionless ratio of dynamic force due to mass flow to the shear stress due to viscosity.

■ **ribbon (girt)**

normally a $1/_4$ inch board let into the studs horizontally to support ceiling or second-floor joists.

■ **ridge**

highest point on the roof, represented by a horizontal line where two roof areas intersect, running the length of the area.

■ **ridge board**

the board placed on edge at the ridge of the roof into which the upper ends of the rafters are fastened.

■ **ridge vent**

a ventilator located at the ridge that allows the escape of warm and/

or moist air from the attic area or rafter cavity. Most ridge vents are either pre-manufactured metal or flexible, shingle-over type.

■ **ridging**

an upward, elongated tenting displacement of a roof membrane frequently occurring over insulation or deck joints. Ridging may be an indication of movement within the roof assembly.

■ **rigid**

ability to resist deformation when subjected to a load; rigidity. The measure of a structure's ability not to change shape when subjected to a load.

■ **rigid pavement**

a pavement which is designed with minimal deflection, i.e.. concrete pavement.

■ **rigidity**

the elasticity of a fluid column.

■ **rip rap**

stone fill manually fit around a structure to prevent erosion of the embankment.

■ **ripple**

a periodic variation of a parameter above or below its mean operating value.

■ **rise**

in stairs, the vertical height of a step or flight of stairs.

■ **rise time**

the elapse of time from the application of a step function input signal for the output to rise from 10% to 90% of the required steady state value.

■ **riser**

each of the vertical boards closing the spaces between the treads of stairways.

■ **risk assessment**

the qualitative and quantitative evaluation performed in an effort to define the risk posed to human health and /or the environment by the presence or potential presence and/or use of specific pollutants.

■ **river**

a natural stream of water of considerable volume.

■ **river basin**

a term used to designate the area drained by a river and its tributaries.

■ **rivet**

a type of metal fastener that connects steel plates together.

■ **roadbase**

a term used to describe crushed rock or natural gravel used in road construction.

Roadway Base being delivered and spread

■ **rock mechanics**

the theoretical and applied science of the physical behaviour of rocks.

■ **rock tunnel**

a passage constructed through solid rock.

■ **rod scraper**

a scraper to remove contaminant build-up and ice from a cylinder rod.

■ **roll roofing**

roofing material, composed of fibre and satin rated with asphalt, that is supplied in 36-inch wide rolls with 108 square feet of material. Weights are generally 45 to 90 pounds per roll.

■ **rolled beam**

steel beams of standard sizes that are produced in large quantities.

■ **roller**

an item of equipment used for compacting pavement material. Types include pneumatic (multi), static, steel or vibrating.

■ **roof**

the assembly of interacting components designed to weatherproof and normally to insulate a buildings surface, separated from adjacent assemblies by walls or changes in elevation.

■ **roof assembly**

an assembly of interacting roof components (includes the roof deck, vapour retarder [if pre-sent], insulation, and roof covering).

■ **roof coating**

a bituminous material, either a cutback or an emulsion, to protect the surface of the burm but not necessarily to re-impregnate it.

■ **roof curb**

raised frame used to mount mechanical units (such as air conditioning or exhaust fans), skylights, etc.

■ **roof deck**

that component in building construction, which forms a platform on which the remainder of the burm components are placed.

■ **roof drain**

the termination or fitting at the roof of an interior drain or leader, for draining rain water from nominally flat roofs.

Clogged Roof Drain

■ **roof sheathing**

the boards or sheet material fastened to the roof rafters on which the shingle or other roof covering is laid.

■ **roof slope**

the angle a roof surface makes with the horizontal, expressed as a ratio of the units of vertical rise to the units of horizontal length (sometimes referred to as run). For English units of measurement, when dimensions are given in inches, slope may be expressed as a ratio of rise to run, such as 4:12, or as a percent.

■ **roof system**

a system of interacting roof components, generally consisting of membrane or primary roof covering and insulation (not including the roof deck) designed to weatherproof and, sometimes, to improve the building's thermal resistance.

■ **roofer**

craftsman who applies roofing materials.

■ **rosin paper (specifically rosin-sized sheathing paper)**

a non-asphaltic paper used as a sheathing paper or slip sheet in some roof systems.

■ **rotary actuator**

a device for converting hydraulic energy into rotary motion a hydraulic motor.

■ **rotary wing landing pad**

a paved or unpaved surface for takeoffs and landings of rotary wing aircraft. It is physically smaller than a rotary wing runway, typically 100 by 100 feet square, and is normally located at a site that is remote from an airfield or heliport. For inventory purposes, only the prepared surface is included.

■ **roto milling**

refer cold planning.

■ **rowlock**

a brick laid on its face edge so that the normal bedding area is visible in the wall face. Frequently spelled rolok.

■ **rubber**

a polymeric material which, at room temperature, is capable of recovering substantially in shape and size after removal of a force. May be natural or synthetic.

■ **rubber seal**

a seal with a polymer (rubber) modified binder (refer seal).

■ **rubber-emulsion paint**

paint, the vehicle of which consists of rubber or synthetic rubber dispersed in fine droplets in water.

■ **rubberised asphalt**

an asphalt in which the binder consists of bitumen modified by the incorporation of rubber, either natural or synthetic or suitable polymer, which helps resist fatigue of asphalt.

■ **rubberised bitumen seal**

a sprayed seal where the binder consists of bitumen modified by the incorporation of rubber, either natural or synthetic.

■ **rule element**

a component and constituent of the regional assessment report.

■ **run**

1. in stairs, the net width of a step or the horizontal distance covered by a flight of stairs.
2. the horizontal distance between the eaves and the ridge of the roof, being half the span for a symmetrical gable roof.

■ **run-off**

Water from rainfall or irrigation that is allowed to flow off the property. Run-off can be thought of as a lost resource and a contributor to nonpoint source pollution.

■ **runway overrun**

a cleared area extending beyond the ends of a runway. These are not normal traffic areas and are intended only to minimise the probability of serious damage to aircraft using these areas accidentally or in cases of emergency.

■ **runway, surfaced**

a flexible or rigid paved airfield surface used for normal takeoffs and landings of fixed or rotary wing aircraft. It can also accommodate rotary wing aircraft.

■ **runway, unsurfaced**

an unpaved, prepared surface for training, emergency, and other special takeoff and landing operations of fixed or rotary wing aircraft. It can also accommodate rotary wing aircraft.

■ **rupture**

failure that is accompanied by significant plastic deformation.

■ **rutting**

the deformation of the pavement surface generally in the wheel path.

■ **saddle**

1. a ridge in the roof deck, whose top divides two sloping parts of the roof so that water will be diverted to the roof drains.
2. two sloping surfaces meeting in a horizontal ridge, used between the back side of a chimney, or other vertical surface, and a sloping roof.

■ **sae numbers**

numbers applied to crank case, transmission, and read axle lubricants to indicate their viscosity range.

■ **safety**

the conservation of human life and its effectiveness, and the prevention of damage to items, consistent with operational requirements.

■ **safety valve**

a highly reliable relief valve not susceptible to silt lock seizure or corrosion. Usually a poppet-type two-way valve intended to release fluid to a secondary area when pressures approach the maximum set value. It serves the same function as a hydraulic fuse that is, to relieve the overpressurisation of a system.

■ **sag curve**

used to describe a vertical curve with a downward approach tangent meeting an upward leaving tangent.

■ **salinity**

the total dissolved solids in water alter all bromide and iodide have been replaced by chloride, and all organic matter has been oxidized. For most purposes, salinity is considered equivalent to total dissolved salt content. Salinity is normally expressed in parts per thousand.

■ **salt water**

water, which contains a relatively high percentage of sodium chloride.

■ **sand asphalt**

asphalt consisting of bitumen and sand.

■ **sand barrier termite protection**

a shallow trench around the perimeter of the house foundation that is filled with sand. Termites cannot pass through the barrier because their tunnels cave in.

■ **sand float finish**

lime mixed with sand, resulting in a textured finish.

■ **sandstone**

sandstones usually can be identified by their coarse, granular, sandy texture. They are sedimentary rocks that consist of consolidated sand grains (mainly quartz and feldspar) cemented together with a variety of minerals (silicates, iron oxides, limonite, calcite and clays). These cementing materials make one sandstone behave very differently from another. Sandstones containing silica are quite hard, strong and decay resistant, whereas those containing calcite resemble limestone in their susceptibility to acid damage, and those containing clay absorb water and deteriorate more easily. Because they have a granular texture throughout, sandstone surfaces stay matte even when worked. Most sandstones have a tendency to absorb moisture and do not withstand frost action well, so they should not be

used as foundation stones and should be protected from excessive moisture.

■ **sap**

a type of fluid contained within a plant.

■ sapwood

the outer zone of wood, next to the bark. In the living tree it contains some living cells (the heartwood contains none), as well as dead and dying cells. In most species, it is lighter coloured than the heartwood. In all species, it is lacking in decay resistance.

■ sash

a single light frame containing one or more lights of glass.

■ sash balance

a device, usually operated by a spring or tensioned weather stripping designed to counterbalance double-hung window sash.

■ saturated felt

a felt which is impregnated with tar or asphalt.

■ saturation

a magnitude limiting condition of the system.

■ saturation, zone of

the zone below the watertable in which all pore spaces are filled with ground water.

■ saw tooth roof

where reviewed from the end, such a roof serrated or tooth profile similar to the teeth of a saw.

■ SC

spiral to curve.

■ scenic waterway

Rivers or river segments chosen for scenic and recreational qualities to be preserved in their natural state.

■ scoring

abrasive damage to slide and sleeve type valves, piston rods, seal glands, seals, piston heads or barrel bore. Scratches in the direction of motion of mechanical parts caused by abrasive contaminants in the fluid.

■ scour

the removal of the soil under and around a structure due to moving water.

■ SCR

a construction aid providing greater efficiency, better workmanship and increased production in masonry construction. It utilises story poles, marked lines and adjustable scaffolding.

■ scratch coat

the first coat of plaster, which is scratched to form a bond for the second coat.

■ screed

1. part of the paved that levels and shapes the asphalt during placing. also refers to a hand held wooden levelling device.
2. a small strip of wood, usually the thickness of the plaster coat, used as a guide for plastering.

■ **screed machine**

a machine that travels along the uncured deck concrete to consolidate and smooth the concrete while also giving it the proper cross slope.

■ **scribing**

fitting woodwork to an irregular surface. in mouldings, cutting the end of one piece to fit the moulded face of the other at an interior angle to replace a miter joint.

■ **scrim**

a woven or mat-type fabric that is used as a membrane sandwich between other material to provide reinforcement and stretch resistance.

■ **scuffing**

a wear mechanism involving microwelding of asperities on contacting surfaces under conditions of high loading and high relative velocities. This microwelding is normally followed by rupture of the welds, roughening and increasing friction.

■ **scupper**

an outlet in the wall of a building or a parapet wall for drainage of water from a flat roof.

■ **SDL**

superimposed deal load. Permanent loads applied after the structural deck behaves compositely with the beams. These loads are due to known sources like railing weight, barrier weight, future wearing surface, etc.

■ **seal**

1. a generic term for a function that prevents or controls the passage of water.
2. to secure a roof or structure from the entry of moisture.

■ **seal compatibility**

the ability of a fluid and an elastomeric material to coexist in intimate contact without the elastomer displaying signs of substantial swelling, hardening or deterioration of mechanical properties.

■ **seal, clearance**

a seal, which limits the leakage between a rotating or reciprocating shaft and a stationary housing, by means of a controlled annular clearance between the two.

■ **seal, dynamic**

a seal used between parts having relative motion.

■ **seal, gasket**

a static seal.

■ **seal, labyrinth**

a clearance-type seal in, which the fluid being sealed must traverse a tortuous path in order to escape.

■ **seal, mechanical**

a seal obtained by mechanical force.

■ **seal, pressure**

a seal obtained by means of fluid pressure.

■ **seal, reciprocating**

a sealing interface that exhibits relative movement of the sealing surfaces by alternately moving forward and backward as in a hydraulic cylinder.

■ **seal, rotary**

a sealing interface in, which relative movement of the sealing surfaces are moving away from each other by rotary action. Normally, it is the shaft that rotates and the casing remains stationary.

■ **seal, static**

a seal used between parts having no relative motion.

■ **seal, windback**

a helically grooved liner, installed either on a stationary member or on a rotating shaft,, which operates through a clearance and tends to lower leakage by means of a pumping action resulting from the transfer of momentum to the fluid.

■ **seal, wiper**

a seal, which operates by a wiping action to remove material from the sealing surfaces.

■ **sealant**

a single- or multi-component polymeric or bituminous-based material used to weatherproof many types of construction joints where moderate movement is expected. The material comes in various grades. Pourable, self-levelling, non-sag, gun grade, and cured or uncured tapes.

■ **sealer**

a finishing material, either clear or pigmented, that is usually applied directly over uncoated wood for the purpose of sealing the surface.

■ **seasoning**

removing moisture from green wood in order to improve its serviceability.

■ **secondary treatment**

purification stage where smaller solids settle out of partially-treated water, and micro-organisms are further broken down by algae and sunlight. After secondary treatment, water is often chlorinated as a last step before it is released from the plant.

■ **sediment**

solid fragmental material that originates from weathering of rocks and is transported or deposited by air, water or ice or by chemical precipitation.

■ **sedimentation**

the removal, transport, and deposition of detached soil particles by flowing water or wind.

■ **seep**

leakage described as recurring fluid not forming a droplet.

■ **seepage**

the appearance and disappearance of water at the ground surface. Seepage designates the type of movement of water in saturated material. It is different from percolation,, which is the predominant type of movement of water in unsaturated material.

■ **segregation**

asphalt, where the coarse aggregate has separated from the fines.

■ **seismic forces**

loads applied to a structure due to an earthquake.

■ **self-adhering membrane**

a membrane that can adhere to a substrate and to itself at overlaps without the use of an additional adhesive. The undersurface of a self-adhering membrane is protected by a release paper or film, which prevents the membrane from bonding to itself during shipping and handling.

■ **self-healing**

a term used in reference to a material which melts with the heat from the sun's rays, and seals over cracks that were earlier formed from other causes.

■ **self-levelling**

a viscous material that is applied by pouring in its uncured state, it spreads out evenly.

■ **selvage**

the unsurfaced strip along a sheet of roll roofing which forms the under portion at the lap in the application of the roof covering.

■ **semi-gloss paint or enamel**

a paint or enamel made with a slight insufficiency of non-volatile vehicle so that its coating, when dry, has some lustre but is not very glossy.

■ **sensitivity, contaminant**

see **omega rating**.

■ **sensitivity, control**

the ratio of controller output response to a specified change in a measured variable; that is, it is the measure of the response of a control unit to a change in the incoming signal. Mathematically, it is the ratio of the response or change induced in the output to a change in the input.

■ **sensor**

a device, which detects a condition in a system and produces an associated signal.

■ **septic tanks**

these are used to hold domestic wastes when a sewer line is not available to carry them to a treatment plant. The wastes are piped to underground tanks directly from a home or homes. Bacteria in the wastes decompose some of the organic matter and sludge settles on the bottom of the tank and the effluent flows out of the tank into the ground through drains.

■ **sequence**

the order in, which various operations in a hydraulic system takes place.

■ **sequence valve**

a pressure operated valve, which automatically diverts flow to a secondary actuator while holding pressure on the primary actuator. Allows one function to take place, one after the other in strict sequence.

■ **service compliance**

used to express how well the 'service integrity' of system satisfies the service requirements includes, not only the power to perform but also to endure.

■ **service integrity**

a quality of a system, which possesses the necessary durability and performance to satisfy its intended purpose.

■ **servomechanism (servo)**

a closed-loop system containing a controller, a feedback element or elements and a servoamplifier. There are three types of hydraulic servomechanisms: the displacement-control system and the valve-control system.

■ **servovalve**

a valve, which automatically modulates its output as a function of the input command.

■ **servovalve null bias**

the input current required to bring the servovalve to null, excluding the effects of valve hysteresis, expressed as percent of rated current.

■ **servovalve null shift**

a change in null bias in a servovalve, expressed as percent of rated current. Null shift may occur with changes in supply pressure, the return pressure, and/or the load pressure drop.

■ **servovalve threshold**

the increment of input current required to produce a change in servovalve output, expressed as percent of rated current. Threshold is normally specified as the current increment required to revert from a condition of increasing output to a condition of decreasing output.

■ **servovalve, flow saturation region**

the region where flow gain decreases with increasing input current, in a servovalve.

■ **servovalve, null region**

The region in a servovalve about null wherein effects of lap in the output stage predominate.

■ **settlement**

the subsidence of a structure caused by compression or movement of the soil below the foundation.

■ **sewage**

water drained by industry and households. Sewage typically contains everything from soap to solid waste, and must be purified before it can be safely returned to the ecosystem.

■ **shake**

a thick hand split shingle, re-sawed to form two shakes; usually edge-grained.

■ **shale**

clay which has been subjected to high pressures until it has hardened.

■ **shear**

a force that causes parts of a material to slide past one another in opposite directions

■ **shear connector**

studs or similar components used to connect the concrete deck to the bridge beams, allowing them to act compositely.

■ **shear force**

the force, which resists the parallel motion of two adjacent planes.

■ **shear walls**

solid concrete walls that resist shear forces; often used in buildings constructed in earthquake zones.

■ **shearing strength**

capacity of an object or soil to resist shearing stresses

■ **sheathing**

1. the boards of sheet type material, plywood or asphalt saturated sheets, nailed to studding or roofing rafters as the base for application of the roof covering.
2. the structural covering, usually wood boards or plywood, used over studs or rafters of a structure. Structural building board is normally wed only as wall sheathing.

■ **shed roof**

a roof having only one slope or pitch, with only one set of rafters which fall from a higher to a lower wall.

■ **sheet metal work**

all components of a house employing sheet metal, such as flashing, gutters, and downspouts.

■ **sheeting**

interlocking rolled steel sheets driven vertically into the ground to retain the soil and allow for the construction of the substructure, also known as sheet piling.

■ **shelf life**

the length of time that a given item can remain in a saleable condition on a supplier's shelf; this is highly relevant for most sealants as they degrade in time even when stored in sealed, unopened containers.

■ **shellac**

a transparent coating made by dissolving lac, a resinous secretion of the lac bug (a scale insect that thrives in tropical countries, especially India), in alcohol.

■ **shim**

thin piece of metal used to make up for any difference in the thickness or elevation of two pieces being joined.

■ **shingle-fashion**

the pattern formed by laying parallel felt rolls with lapped joints so that one longitudinal edge overlaps the longitudinal edge on the adjacent felts. Shingle fashion application begin at the low point on a roof so that one ply drains water to a lower one and so on to a drain or to the roof edge.

■ **shingles**

1. small units of material which are laid in a series of overlapping rows as a roof covering on pitched roofs.
2. roof covering of asphalt. Asbestos, wood, tile, slate, or other material cut to stock lengths, widths, and thickness.

■ **shingles, siding**

various kinds of shingles, such as wood shingles or shakes and nonwood shingles, that are used over sheathing for exterior sidewall covering of a structure.

■ **shock wave**

a pressure wave front, which moves at a supersonic velocity.

■ **shoring**

temporary supporting members for concrete formwork and structure stability.

■ **shoulder**

the outside section of the pavement which is generally not trafficked.

■ **shoved joints**

vertical joints filled by shoving a brick against the next brick when it is being laid in a bed of mortar.

■ **shoving**

movement of the pavement generally caused by heavy traffic.

■ **shrinkage**

1. decrease in size which may result in cracking, stresses, strain.
2. if scratches or substrate imperfections have not been properly filled, they will show up as the paint shrinks into them.
3. decrease in wood dimensions due to water loss the wood cell walls. Shrinkage across the grain of wood occurs when the moisture content falls below the fibre saturation point (28-30 percent). Below the fibre saturation point, shrinkage is generally proportional to moisture content. Shrinkage is expressed as a percentage of the green wood dimensions.
4. decrease in volume of a soil (or fill) material through the reduction of voids by mechanical compaction, superimposed loads, or natural consolidation; settling or reduction in volume of earthen fills, cement slurries, or concrete on setting; decrease in volume of clayey soil or sediment due to reduction of void volume, principally by drying. 5. cracking due to drying.

■ **shrinkage crack**

a crack produced in fine-grained sediment or rock by the loss of contained water during drying or dehydration; e.g., a desiccation crack or a mud crack.

■ **shrinkage index**

the numerical difference between the plastic and shrinkage limits.

■ **shutter**

usually lightweight louvered or flush wood or non-wood frames in the form of doors located at each side of a window. Some are made to close over the window for protection; others are fastened to the wall as a decorative device.

■ **side lap**

the continuous longitudinal overlap of neighbouring like materials.

■ **siding**

the finish covering of the outside wall of a frame building, whether made of horizontal weatherboards, vertical boards with battens, shingles, or other material.

■ **siding, bevel (lap siding)**

wedge-shaped boards used as horizontal siding in a lapped pattern. This siding varies in butt thickness from ½ to ¾ inch and in widths up to 12 inches. Normally used over some type of sheathing.

■ **siding, dolly varden**

bevelled wood siding which is rebutted on the bottom edge.

■ **siding, drop**

usually ¾ inch thick and 6 and 8 inches wide with tongued-and-grooved or shiplap edges. Often used as siding without sheathing in secondary buildings.

■ **sign anchor**

a component usually formed with steel angles which penetrates the bur and is fastened to the deck.

■ **signal**

a command or indication of a desired position or velocity; that is, information that is transmitted from one point in a system to another.

■ **signing**

traffic signs that are usually included in the M&PT.

■ **sill**

the lowest member of the frame of a structure, resting on the foundation and supporting the floor joists or the uprights of the wall. The member forming the lower side of an opening, as a door sill, window sill, etc.

■ **siltation**

the deposition of finely divided soil and rock particles upon the bottom of stream and river beds and reservoirs.

■ **single ply**

a descriptive term signifying a roof membrane composed of only one layer of material such as EPDM, hypalon or PVC.

■ **single size aggregate**

an aggregate having a major proportion of particles lying between narrow size limits.

■ **single tee**

the name given to a type of precast concrete deck which has one stiffening rib integrally cast into slab.

■ **single-ply membranes**

roofing membranes that are field applied using just one layer of membrane material (either homogeneous or composite) rather than multiple layers.

■ **single-ply system**

generally, there are six types of single-ply roofing systems: 1) fully-adhered 2) Loose-laid 3) mechanically-fastened 4) partially-adhered 5) protected membrane roof 6) self-adhering

■ **SIP forms**

stay-in-place forms. Corrugated light gauge metal forms that span between bridge members and serve as the form for the deck concrete and remain in place after the concrete has cured.

■ **site**

the physical grouping of a number of roofs or buildings at a geographical location.

■ **skid resistance**

the measurement of the resistance of a pavement surface to skidding.

■ **sky dome**

a type of sky lite exhibiting a characteristic translucent plastic domed top.

■ **skylight**

a structure on a roof that is designed to admit light and is somewhat above the plane of the roof surface.

■ **slag**

by product of steel making, crushed and screened as aggregate.

■ **slate**

a dark grey stratified stone cut relatively thin and installed on pitched roofs in a shingle like fashion.

■ **sleeper**

usually, a wood member embedded in concrete, as in a floor, that serves to support and to fasten sub floor or flooring.

■ **sleet**

precipitation, which is a mixture of rain and ice.

■ **slenderness ratio**

a term that describes the geometry of a column undergoing compression and is defined as the effective length of the rod divided by the radius of gyration.

■ **slip**

internal leakage of liquid under pressure in a component such as in a pump or actuator.

■ **slipform**

process of pouring concrete into a moving form. The concrete has a low slump so that the concrete does not lose the shape of the form.

■ **slippage**

it is the sliding, lateral movement between adjacent to plies of felt along the plane of the bitumen film separating them, which results in a randomly wrinkled appearance.

■ **slope**

incline or pitch of roof surface.

■ **slope failure**

gradual or rapid downslope movement of soil or rock under gravitational stress, often as a result of man-made factors such as removal of material from the base of a slope.

■ **slope protection**

material that prevents erosion of an embankment slope.

■ **sludge**

an insoluble material formed as a result either of deterioration reactions in an oil or by contamination of an oil.

■ **slump**

a measure of the flowability of a batch of concrete.

■ **slurry seal**

a road surface treatment involving the application of a mixture of fine aggregate (5 mm or 7 mm) and emulsion in the form of a slurry over an existing pavement.

■ **slurry wall**

barriers used to contain the flow of contaminated fund water or subsurface liquid. Slurry walls are constructed by digging a trench around a contaminated area and filling the trench with an impermeable material that prevents water from passing through it. The ground water or contaminated liquids trapped within the area surrounded by the slurry wall can be exacted and treated.

■ **slushed joints**

vertical joints filled, after units are laid, by 'throwing' mortar in with the edge of a trowel.

■ **smooth surface texture**

the surface shows spray undulation and is ideal for receiving a protective coating. Even though the surface texture is classified as smooth, the theoretical coverage rate cannot be used without adding a minimum of 5% additional material to adequately cover the undulation.

■ **smooth surfaced roof**

a roof membrane without mineral granule or aggregate surfacing.

■ **Splitting**

a rupture (generally linear) or tear in a material or membrane resulting from tensile forces.

■ **snow**

precipitation in the form of branched hexagonal crystals, often mixed with simple ice crystals,, which fall more or less continuously from a solid cloud sheet. These crystals may fall either separately or in cohesive clusters forming snowflakes.

■ **snow course**

a line laid out and permanently marked on a drainage area along, which the snow is sampled at definite distances or stations. Sampling occurs at appropriate times to determine snow depth, water equivalent, and density.

■ **snow density**

ratio between the volume of melt water derived from a sample of snow and the initial volume of the sample.

■ **snow field**

an area, usually at high elevation or in polar latitudes, where snow accumulates and remains throughout the entire year.

■ **snow survey**

the process or operation of determining the depth, water content, and density of snow at various selected points on a drainage basin. This is done in order to determine the amount of water stored there in the form of snow for the purpose of forecasting runoff.

■ **snowfall**

the amount of snow, hail, sleet, or other precipitation occurring in solid form, which reaches the earth's surface. It may be expressed in depth in inches after it falls, or in terms of inches in depth of the equivalent amount of water.

■ **snowflake**

precipitation, which is made up of a number of snow crystals fused together.

■ **snowpack**

the winter accumulation of snow in mountain areas.

■ **SO₄**

sulphate.

■ **soaker hose**

low-flow watering device with small holes throughout the surface of the hose. Good for plant beds and gardens.

■ **soap**

a masonry unit of normal face dimensions, having a nominal 2 inches thickness.

■ **soffit**

the underside of a part or member of a building extending out from the plane of the building walls. Usually the underside of an overhanging cornice.

■ **soft-burned**

clay products which have been fired at low temperature ranges, producing relatively high absorptions and low compressive strengths.

■ **softening point**

the temperature at which a substance changes from a hard material to a softer and more viscous material.

■ **soft-ground tunnels**

a passage constructed through loose, unstable, or wet ground, requiring supports to keep the walls from collapsing.

■ **soil cover (ground cover)**

a light covering of plastic film, roll roofing, or similar material used over the soil in crawl spaces of buildings to minimise moisture permeation of the area.

■ **soil mechanics**

the application of the principles of mechanics and hydraulics to engineering problems dealing with the behaviour and nature of soils, sediments and other unconsolidated accumulations of soil particles

■ **soil moisture (soil water)**

water diffused in the soil. It is found in the upper part of the zone of aeration from which water is discharged by transpiration from plants or by soil evaporation.

■ **soil moisture sensor**

a device, which can be attached to any automatic irrigation system that monitors level drops below the desired level.

■ **soil stack**

a general term for the vertical main of a system of soil, waste, or vent piping.

■ **solar screen**

a perforated wall used as a sunshade.

■ **soldier**

a stretcher set on end with face showing on the wall surface.

■ **sole plate**

the top steel plate of a bearing that attaches to the bottom flange of the girder.

■ **solid**

a state of matter, neither liquid or gas. The solid state of water is ice.

■ **solid bridging**

a solid member placed between adjacent floor joists near the centre of the span to prevent joists from twisting.

■ **sound pressure level**

is the ratio of the sound pressure generated by a noise source with respect to a reference sound pressure expressed in decibel scale.

■ **sound transmission control stack effect**

results from the difference in air temperature between indoor and outdoor air during the heating season. Warm air, being lighter than cold air, rises in a building, creating a suction at the base and exerting an outward pressure at the top. The higher the building, the greater the pressure difference across the walls and roof. The suction is greatest at the base, decreasing as the building rises to a neutral pressure plane somewhere between the ground floor and the roof. Above the neutral pressure plane the pressure becomes positive (active outwards) and increases with height, reaching its highest value at the roof. The quantity of air entering the building below the neutral pressure plane is equal to the quantity of air leaving the building above that level

■ **sounding**

a method of checking for voids or delaminations in concrete by striking a hammer against the structure and listening for a hollow sound.

■ **spall**

a small fragment removed from the face of a masonry unit by a blow or by action of the elements.

■ **spalling**

the chipping or flaking of concrete, bricks, or other masonry where improper drainage or venting and freeze/thaw cycling exists.

span

1. the horizontal distance between supporting structures such as beams, trusses or columns.
2. the distance between structural supports such as walls, columns, piers, beams, girders, and trusses.

special purpose work holding devices and machinery

precision-made mass production tooling but also includes robotic arm end effectors (grippers/holders) for use on industrial robots. Special purpose machines/equipment may also be manufactured to carry-out specific tasks on a mass production line such as winding electric motors, assembling bearing assemblies, filling bottles and cans, or any other automated process

specific gravity

the ratio of the density of a given volume of fluid to the density of an equal volume of water at reference conditions.

specific heat

the heat capacity of a material per unit mass. The amount of heat (in calories) required to raise the temperature of one gram of a substance $1°C$; the specific heat of water is 1 calorie.

specific weight

the weight per unit volume of a substance.

specification

detailed written instructions which, when clear and concise, explains each phase of work to be done.

spill

to cause or allow to run or fall from a container unintentionally so as to be lost or wasted. It is also the overflow from a reservoir after it is full.

spillway

an overflow channel that allows dam operators to release lake water when it gets high enough to threaten the safety of a dam.

spire

an architectural or decorative feature of a skyscraper; the council on tall buildings and urban habitat includes spires but not antennae when calculating the official height of a skyscraper.

splash block

a small masonry block laid with the top close to the ground surface to receive roof drainage from downspouts and to carry it away from the building.

splice

the joining of two members to allow them to act like a continuous member.

splitting

the formation of long cracks completely through a roof membrane. Splits are frequently associated with lack of allowance for expansion stresses. They can also be a result of deck deflection or change in deck direction.

spillway

The channel or passageway around or over a dam through, which excess water is diverted.

■ **spool**

any cylindrical shaped part of a hydraulic component, which controls the flow passing through the component in accordance with its movement.

■ **spool valve, critical-lapped**

a valve in which the spool land width is identical to the port width. This is also called a zero lapped.

■ **spool valve, matched**

a four-way valve in which all orifice areas are equal in either direction of spool travel.

■ **spool valve, overlapped**

a valve in which the spool lands are wider than the ports, thus producing a dead zone or band at neutral.

■ **spool valve, symmetrical**

see matched spool valve.

■ **spool valve, underlapped**

a valve in which the spool lands are narrower than the ports.

■ **spray seal**

a process of spraying bitumen followed by the spreading and rolling of aggregate (ranging from 5 mm to 20 mm) which adheres to the bitumen to form a final trafficable surface. Can be placed directly over the prime, previous seal (rehabilitation), asphalt or crushed rock.

■ **spring**

a concentrated discharge of ground water coming out at the surface as flowing water.

■ **spring rate**

the ratio of the force applied on a spring to the deflection of the spring from its equilibrium position as predicted by Hooke's law.

■ **spring runoff**

snow melting in the spring causes water bodies to rise. This in streams and rivers is called 'spring runoff'.

■ **spud**

the removal of gravel or heavy accumulations of bitumen from roof membranes by means of chipping or scraping

■ **square**

1. a term used by the roof industry to indicate an amount of roof area equal to 100 square feet.
2. a unit of measure—100 square feet—usually applied to roofing material. Sidewall coverings are sometimes packed to cover 100 square feet and are sold on that basis.

■ **ST**

spiral to tangent

■ **stabilisation**

the process' of changing an active substance into inert, harmless material, or physical activities at a site that act to limit the further spread of contamination without actual reduction of toxicity.

■ **stabilise**

the addition of a material e.g.. cement, lime, fines etc. To improve the characteristics of the original material.

■ **stability**

the resistance of a substance to permanent changes in its physical or chemical properties under normal storage and use conditions.

■ **stable**

ability to resist collapse and deformation; stability. Characteristic of a structure that is able to carry a realistic load without collapsing or deforming significantly.

■ **stack**

1. any structure or part thereof which contains a flue or flues for the discharge of gases.
2. a vertical pipe projecting through a bur that carries off smoke or gases.

■ **stage construction**

construction done so that traffic may be maintained on a portion of an existing structure while a longitudinal section of a new structure is constructed. Traffic is then shifted over to that portion of the new structure while the existing structure is removed and the new structure is completed.

■ **stain, shingle**

a form of oil paint, very thin in consistency, intended for colouring wood with rough surfaces, such as shingles, without forming a coating of significant thickness or gloss.

■ **stair carriage**

supporting member for stair treads. Usually, a 2-inch plank notched to receive the treads; sometimes called a 'rough horse'.

■ **standard**

a pre-mixed solution with a known amount of material to be tested; can be used for calibration but also to check monitoring accuracy.

■ **standing seam**

a metal roof system that consists of an overlapping or interlocking seam that occurs at an upturned rib. The standing seam may be made by turning up the edges of two adjacent metal panels and overlapping them, then folding or interlocking them in a variety of ways.

■ **starter strips**

in the construction of the bur the narrow strips of roofing felts, cut from standard width rolls, that are applied at the beginning point so as to assure uniform configuration of the specified number of plies.

■ **starting torque**

the pressure required to bring an energy converter from its inoperative condition into motion.

■ **static error**

the error of a servomechanism with a fixed applied signal, usually due to friction or load effects.

■ **static load**

in roofing the total amount of permanent non moving weight that is applied to given surface areas.

■ **static pressure**

pressure in a fluid at rest.

■ **station**

term used to describe the location along a roadway alignment.

■ **stationarity time**

also known as 'standing time'. It is the time for which a valve spool remains stationary.

■ **STC (sound transmission class)**

a measure of sound stopping of ordinary noise.

■ **steam**

the vapour that forms when water is heated to the boiling point. Steam under pressure is capable of driving a piston in a piston engine or turning the blade of a turbine.

■ **steam, dry**

a steam that is so hot that no water droplets are present in it.

■ **steel**

an alloy of iron and carbon that is hard, strong, and malleable.

■ **stem**

the part of the abutment above the footing and below the backwall.

■ **step input function**

an instantaneous increase in an input variable.

■ **sterilisation**

a cleansing process that removes possible contamination by bacteria; used with faecal coliform testing equipment.

■ **stick-slip**

a jerky relative motion between sliding contacts under boundary lubrication conditions. This situation prevails when the static coefficient of friction is higher than the kinetic value. Normally, the addition of a friction modifier can eliminate the problem by ensuring that the kinetic coefficient is greater than the static friction coefficient. See **ratchetting**.

■ **stiction**

it is the force required to initiate movement. The static friction that tends to prevent relative motion between two movable parts.

■ **stiff**

ability to resist deformation; stiffness. The measure of a structure's capacity to resist deformation.

■ **stiffener**

a metal plate welded to the web of a steel beam to improve the resistance to buckling of the web.

■ **stile**

an upright framing member in a panel door.

■ **stirrup**

a 'U' shaped reinforcing bar normally placed transverse to the axis of concrete beam to resist flexural shear.

■ **stone fill**

stone that is dumped around an abutment or pier to prevent erosion of the embankment.

■ **stone mastic asphalt (SMA)**

asphalt with special grading and binders to produce high rutting resistance.

■ **stool**

a flat moulding fitted over the window sill between jambs and contacting the bottom rail of the lower sash.

■ storm

a change in the ordinary conditions of the atmosphere, which may include any or all meteorological disturbances such as wind, rain, snow, hail, or thunder.

■ storm sash or storm window

an extra window usually placed outside of an existing one, as additional protection against cold weather.

■ storm sewer

a sewer that carries only surface runoff, street wash, and snow melt from the land. In a separate sewer system, storm sewers are completely separate from those that carry domestic and commercial wastewater.

■ stormwater drainage system

man-made and natural features, which function as a system to collect, convey, channel, hold, inhibit, retain, detain, infiltrate, or divert stormwater runoff.

■ story

that part of a building between any floor and the floor or roof next above.

■ storey pole

a marked pole for measuring masonry coursing during construction.

■ strain alleviating membrane interlayer

a modified bituminous layer applied immediately below the wear-ing course to absorb reflective cracking from the underlying layers.

■ strainer

a coarse filter often used in pump suction lines, normally contains wire-cloth media.

■ straw bale technique

a building technique for exterior walls where straw (not hay) bales are stacked, reinforced and interlocked in a manner that forms a thick, highly insulated wall.

■ straw-mud

this is an old building technique for exterior walls where earth material is mixed with straw, moistened and pressed between forms where it hardens into a strong wall. It is then covered with a waterproofing plaster system.

■ stream

a general term for a body of flowing water. In hydrology the term is generally applied to the water flowing in a natural channel as distinct from a canal. More generally, it is applied to the water flowing in any channel, natural or artificial. Some types of streams
1. *Ephemeral*
a stream, which flows only in direct response to precipitation, and whose channel is at all times above the water table.
2. intermittent or seasonal a stream, which flows only at certain times of the year when it receives water from springs, rainfall, or from surface sources such as melting snow.

3. *perennial*
a stream, which flows continuously.

4. *Gaining*
a stream or reach of a stream that receives water from the zone of saturation. An effluent stream.

5. *Insulated*
a stream or reach of a stream that neither contributes water to the zone of saturation nor receives water from it. It is separated from the zones of saturation by an impermeable bed.

6. *Losing*
a stream or reach of a stream that contributes water to the zone of saturation. An influent stream.

7. *Perched*
a perched stream is either a losing stream or an insulated stream that is separated from the underlying ground water by a zone of aeration.

8. *swamps*
shallow lakes where a small depth of water and a slight range of fluctuation permits the growth of aquatic vegetation.

■ **stream gauging**

a process of determining the rate of flow, or the discharge, of streams.

■ **stream segment**

surface waters of an approved planning area exhibiting common biological, chemical, hydrological, natural, and physical characteristics and processes. Segments will normally exhibit common reactions to external stresses (e.g. discharge or pollutants). Segments are enumerated using a four digit number. The first two digits identify the basin in, which the segment is located. The last two digits distinguish the segments within a particular river, coastal or estuarine basin. Boundaries of bay and estuarine segments (identified with the number 24 as the first two digits) have not been precisely defined and are illustrated as approximations at this time.

■ **streamflow**

the discharge that occurs in a natural channel. Although the term discharge can be applied to the flow of a canal, the word streamflow uniquely describes the discharge in a surface stream course. The term 'streamflow' is more general than runoff, as stream flow may be applied to discharge whether or not it is affected by diversion or regulation.

■ **streamflow depletion**

The amount of water that annually flows into a valley or onto a particular land area minus the amount that flows out of the valley or away from the particular land area. It is also the amount of water taken from a stream.

■ **stretcher**

a masonry unit laid with its greatest dimension horizontal and its face parallel to the wall face.

■ **string, stringer**

a timber or other support for cross members in floors or ceilings. In stairs, the support on which the stair treads rest also stringboard.

■ **stringing mortar**

the procedure of spreading enough mortar on a bed to lay several masonry units.

■ **strip flooring**

wood flooring consisting of narrow, matched strips.

■ **stripping**

the loss of aggregates from a spray seal surface or the loss of binder from the surface of the aggregate in asphalt.

■ **stroke**

the linear movement of a valve spool, cylinder rod, or pump/motor displacement element that establishes the limits of motion.

■ **strong**

ability to carry a realistic load; strength. the measure of a structure's ability to carry a realistic load.

■ **struck joint**

any mortar joint which has been finished with a trowel.

■ **structural engineer**

an engineer who investigates the behavior and design of all kinds of structures, including dams, domes, tunnels, bridges, and skyscrapers, to make sure they are safe and sound for human use.

■ **structural integrity**

the component must itself be capable of resisting the imposed load or must be supported by one that can. It must be capable of resisting the strongest loads or combinations acting directly or indirectly on it without rupturing or detaching itself away from its supported and supporting elements, or fail in creep. The component must be sufficiently rigid to resist displacement.

■ **structural lifting**

See **Jacking**

■ **strut**

bracing inside a deep sheeted excavation or cofferdam which spans between opposite sides of the enclosure. Struts are connected to wales to keep the excavation open. See also, **wale**.

■ **stucco**

most commonly refers to an outside plaster made with port-land cement as its base.

■ **stud**

one of a series of slender wood or metal vertical structural members placed as supporting elements in walls and partitions.

■ **subbase**

the material placed immediately over the subgrade.

■ **subfloor**

boards or plywood laid on joists over which a finish floor is to be laid.

■ **subgrade**

quarry and sand products.

■ **subplate**

a manifold base on, which surface-mounted valves are attached and through, which fluid connections are made.

■ **substrate**

the surface upon which the roofing or waterproofing membrane is applied (e.g., in roofing, the structural deck or insulation).

■ **substructure**

any supporting member below the superstructure (e.g.,abutments, piers, wingwalls, etc.).

■ **subsurface water**

all water, which occurs below the ground surface.

■ **suction head**

the vertical distance between the fluid level in the reservoir and the pump inlet along with any reservoir pressure usually specified by the pump manufacturer according to the pump design.

■ **suction line**

the conduit between the reservoir and the pump.

■ **sulphur dioxide(SO₂)**

a colourless, irritating gas that is a primary cause of acid rain. It is a by-product of coal combustion.

■ **sump**

a reservoir sometimes forming part of a roof drain. A depression in the roof deck of a building at a roof and delivery it to the drain.

■ **superelevation**

the cross slope of a roadway at a horizontal curve.

■ **superstructure**

That part of the structure above, and supported by the bearings.

■ **surcharge**

load that acts on a retaining wall in addition to normal soil forces, e.g., a vehicular load or a building load, etc.

■ **surface tension**

the tendency of liquid molecules to pull together at any surface to form the smallest possible area. The tension that a given liquid is capable of developing before it ruptures is called its 'surface tension.' It is expressed in dynes per centimetre or ergs per square centimetre.

■ **surface water**

Lakes, bays, ponds, impounding reservoirs, springs, rivers, streams, creeks, estuaries, wetlands, marshes, inlets, canals, gulfs inside the territorial limits of the state, and all other bodies of surface water, natural or artificial, inland or coastal, fresh or salt, navigable or non-navigable, and including the beds and banks of all watercourses and bodies of surface water, that are wholly or partially inside or bordering the state or subject to the jurisdiction of the state; except that waters in treatment systems, which are authorised by state or federal law, regulation, or permit, and, which are created for the purpose of waste treatment are not considered to be waters in the state.

■ **surfacing**

the top layer or layers of a roof covering, specified or designed to protect the underlying roofing from direct exposure to the weather.

■ **surge**

a momentary uncontrolled rapid rise in pressure or flow usually resulting from opening or closing of a valve or a change in loading conditions.

■ **suspended ceiling**

a ceiling system supported by hanging it from the overhead structural framing.

■ **suspended water**

water in the zone of aeration, which includes seeping water and stored water.

■ **suspension bridge**

a bridge in which the roadway deck is suspended from cables that pass over two towers; the cables are anchored in housings at either end of the bridge.

■ **swashplate**

an inclined disk or plate in an axial piston pump or motor, which causes the pistons to reciprocate as the cylinder barrel rotates. The swashplate angle can be adjusted to vary the displacement of the pistons.

■ **swell**

the increased volume of a seal or elastomer caused by immersion in or contact with a fluid.

■ **system**

a collection of parts or components arranged in some order according to a rational set of principles or natural laws and used for the independent execution of some task.

■ **system effectiveness**

the probability or chance that a system can successfully meet an operational demand within a given time when operated under specified conditions.

■ **system pressure**

nominal pressure usually measured at the inlet to the first valve or at the pump outlet.

■ **system protector**

a safety device that provides pressure protection when an overload pressure condition occurs a safety valve function. One such device is equipped with a frangible disk, which ruptures at a preset value of pressure. Unlike relief valves, they do not automatically reset themselves they require a fractured part to be replaced (e.g., a disc or a nail). See also 'Hydraulic Fuse' for excess flow protection.

■ **systemic**

pertaining to or affecting a system, such that the body or system is affected as a whole.

■ **tab**

the exposed portion of strip shingles defined by cutouts.

■ **tack coat**

1. the spraying of a binder such as bitumen or emulsion as a thin film to improve the adhesion between layers of asphalt.
2. an application of material to a surface, to prevent slippage planes and to provide a bond between the existing surface and the new surfacing.

■ **tack range**

an application of material to a surface, to prevent slippage planes and to provide a bond between the existing surface and the new surfacing

■ **tail beam**

a relatively short beam or joist supported in a wall on one end and by a header at the other.

■ **tank**

a storage vessel used to contain and supply make-up fluid to a hydraulic system. It is a passive container for hydraulic fluid.

■ **tapered edge strip**

a tapered insulation strip used to 1. elevate and slope the roof at the perimeter and at curbs, and 2. provide a gradual transition from one layer of insulation to another.

■ **tar**

a brown or black bituminous material, liquid or semi-solid in consistency, in which the predominating constituents are bitumens obtained as condensates in the processing of coal, petroleum, oil-shale, wood, or other organic materials.

■ **taxiways**

pavements used for the powered ground movement of aircraft between runway systems and other airfield facilities.

■ **tear off**

a term used to describe the complete removal of the built up roof membrane and insulation down to and exposing the roof deck.

■ **tear resistance**

the load required to tear a material, when the stress is concentrated on a small area of the material by the introduction of a prescribed flaw or notch. Expressed in psi (pounds force) per inch width or kN/m (kilonewton per meter width).

■ **technical ceramic**

a ceramic that exhibits a high degree of industrial efficiency through carefully designed microstructures and superb dimensional precision.

■ **telltale**

an outward sign of a condition a precursor.

■ **temper**

to moisten and mix clay, plaster or mortar to a proper consistency.

■ **temporary structure**

a pedestrian and/or vehicular bridge built to carry traffic around an active construction site in lieu of stage construction. The structure will be removed after the new bridge is open to traffic.

■ **tender mix**

an asphalt mix that moves easily and is susceptible to rutting by traffic.

■ **tensegrity**

an array of tension cables and compression rods that supports a structure; invented by Kenneth Snellson.

■ **tension**

a stretching force that pulls on a material.

■ **tension ring**

a support ring that resists the outward force pushing against the lower sides of a dome.

■ **termination**

the treatment or method of anchoring and/or sealing the free edges of the membrane in a roofing or waterproofing system.

■ **termite shield**

a shield, usually of non-corrodible metal, placed in or on a foundation wall or other mass of masonry or around pipes to prevent passage of termites.

■ **termites**

insects that superficially resemble ants in size, general appearance, and habit of living in colonies; hence, they are frequently called 'white ants.' subterranean termites establish themselves in buildings not by being carried in with lumber, but by entering from ground nests after the building has been constructed.

■ **terneplate**

sheet iron or steel coated with an alloy of lead and tin.

■ **test cut**

a sample of the roof, which may contain all components or just the membrane, usually used to diagnose the condition of the existing membrane, evaluate the type and number of plies or number of membranes, or rates of application such as determine the weight of the average inter-ply bitumen moppings.

■ **thalweg**

a line connecting the lowest points along a stream bed or valley.

■ **thermal chimney**

a section of a building where solar heat or thermal currents are controlled in a manner that stimulates an updraft and the exhaust of heated air. This draws in fresh air to occupied areas of the building through open windows or vents and is a passive cooling method.

■ **thermal envelope**

the shell of a building that essentially creates a barrier from the elements. A highly insulated thermal envelope allows maximum control of interior temperatures with minimal outdoor influence.

■ **thermal mass**

materials that absorb hear or coolness and store if for a long period of time. Water and masonry materials can provide thermal mass. Such materials react slowly to temperature variations and are important aspects of any passive heating or cooling system.

■ **thermal movement**

the measured amount of dimensional change, a material exhibits as it is warmed or cooled.

■ **thermal performance tie**

any unit of material which connects masonry to masonry or other materials.

■ **thermal pollution**

the degradation of water quality by the introduction of a heated effluent. It is primarily the result of the discharge of cooling waters from industrial processes, particularly from electrical power generation. Waste heat eventually results from virtually every energy conversion.

■ **thermal shock**

the stress-producing phenomenon resulting from sudden temperature changes in a roof membrane when, for example, a cold rain shower follows brilliant hot sunshine, which may result in sudden cooling or rapid contraction of the membrane.

■ **thermal stability**

a measure of the chemical stability of a fluid subjected to high temperatures and includes resistance to molecular scission or cracking. For hydraulic fluids, this property is principally a criterion for the stability of additives.

■ **thermoplastic material**

solid material which is softened by increasing temperatures and hardened by decreasing temperatures.

■ **thin-film lubrication**

a condition in which the film thickness of the lubricant is such that the friction between the surfaces is determined by the properties of the surfaces as well as the viscosity of the lubricant.

■ **threshold**

a strip of wood or metal with bevelled edges used over the finish floor and the sill of exterior doors.

■ **throttle**

a restriction to the normal flow of fluid.

■ **throttling**

the regulation of flow through a restriction or valve where the velocity must increase.

■ **throttling process**

an adiabatic, irreversible process in which a fluid flows from a region of constant high pressure through a restriction to a region of constant lower pressure such that no heat can flow into or out of the system.

■ **through-wall flashing**

a water-resistant material, which may be metal or membrane, extending through a wall and its cavities, positioned to direct water entering the top of the wall or cavity to the exterior, usually through weep holes.

■ **tidal power**

a form of power obtained from the filling and emptying of a bay or an estuary that can be closed by a dam. The enclosed basin is allowed to fill and empty only during brief periods at high and low tides in order to develop as much power as possible.

■ **tides**

the rise and fall of the surface of oceans, seas, bays, rivers, and other water bodies caused by the gravitational attraction of the moon and sun occurring unequally on different parts of the earth.

■ **tie-in**

a term used to describe the joining of a new roof with the old.

■ **tie-off**

(in roofing and waterproofing) the transitional seal used to terminate a roofing or waterproofing application at the top or bottom of flashings, or by forming a watertight seal with the substrate, membrane or adjacent roofing or waterproofing system.

■ **tilt-up wall**

cast concrete units which are preformed which, when cured, are tilted to their vertical position and secured by mechanical fasteners to prior erected structural steel.

■ **time constant**

the elapsed time from the application of a step function input signal until the output signal reaches 63.2% of the required steady state value.

■ **titrant**

a solution of known strength or concentration; used in titration.

■ **titration**

a process whereby a solution of known strength (titrant) is added to a certain volume of treated sample containing an indicator. A colour change shows when the reaction is complete.

■ **titrator**

an instrument, usually a calibrated cylinder (tube-form), used in titration to measure the amount of titrant being added to the sample.

■ **toenailing**

to drive a nail at a slant with the initial surface in order to permit it to penetrate into a second member.

■ **tooling**

compressing and shaping the face of a mortar joint with a special tool other than a trowel.

■ **toothing**

constructing the temporary end of a wall with the end stretcher of every alternate course projecting. Projecting units are tooters.

■ **top mopping**

the finished mopping of hot bitumen on a built-up roof.

■ **torching**

applying direct flame to a membrane for the purpose of melting, heating or adhering.

■ **torque**

a rotary thrust or force. A measure of rotary force or turning effort that is usually expressed in poundforce feet (lbf ft) or Newton metres (Nm) where 0.74 Nm = 1.0 lbf ft.

■ **torque converter**

a rotary fluid coupling that is capable of multiplying torque.

■ **torque motor**

an electromagnetic device that provides actuation of a spring-restrained armature, either rotary or translatory.

■ **torsion**

an action that twists a material.

■ **total dissolved solids**

the amount of material (inorganic salts and small amounts of organic material) dissolved in water and commonly expressed as a concentration in terms of milligrams per liter.

■ **total suspended solids**

total suspended matter in water,, which is commonly expressed as a concentration in terms of milligrams per liter.

■ **total toxicity**

toxicity as determined by exposing aquatic organisms to samples

or dilutions of instream water or treated effluent. Also referred to as whole fluent toxicity.

■ **toxic materials**

any liquid, gaseous, or solid substance or substances in a concentration, which, when applied to, discharged to, or deposited in the waters in the state, may exert a poisonous effect detrimental to man or to the propagation, cultivation or conservation of animals, fish, or other aquatic life.

■ **toxicity**

the occurrence of lethal or sublethal adverse effects on representative, sensitive organisms due to exposure to toxic materials. Adverse effects caused by conditions of temperature, dissolved oxygen, or non-toxic dissolved substances are excluded from the definition of toxicity.

■ **trace**

the amount of rainfall or other form of precipitation, which occurs when the quantity is so small that it cannot be measured in the rain gauge.

■ **tractive effort**

the force delivered to the contact point with the ground and includes all mechanical losses.

■ **traditional masonry**

masonry in which design is based on empirical rules which control minimum thickness, lateral support requirements and height without a structural analysis.

■ **transducer**

a component used to convert one form of energy into another, e.g., pressure into electrical voltage.

■ **transfer function**

an expression stating the relation between an input signal and a corresponding output signal, the relation involving both the magnitude and the timing of the signal.

■ **transpiration**

the process by, which water vapour escapes from the living plant, principally the leaves, and enters the atmosphere.

■ **tread**

the horizontal board in a stairway on which the foot is placed.

■ **tremie**

a pipe or funnel used for placing concrete under water.

■ **tremie seal**

a special concrete mixture that is placed under water for the purpose of sealing the bottom of a sheeted excavation surrounded by water.

■ **tribology**

The science and technology of friction, lubrication and wear. Officially known as the study of interacting surfaces in relative motion and all related engineering problems including the subjects and practices of friction, lubrication, and wear.

■ **tributary**

A stream or other body of water, surface or underground, which contributes its water, even though intermittently and in small quantities, to another and larger stream or body of water.

■ **trim**

the finish materials in a building, such as mouldings applied around openings (window trim, door trim) or at the floor and ceiling of rooms (baseboard, cornice, and other mouldings).

■ **trimmer**

a beam or joist to which a header is nailed in framing for a chimney, stairway, or other opening.

■ **tropical hardwood**

wood products harvested from tropical rain forests. Tropical forests are not being harvested in a well-managed manner except in a few isolated cases. Certification efforts indicating sustainably harvested woods are just beginning.

■ **troposphere**

the layer of atmosphere closest to the earth, extending seven to ten miles above the earth. It usually contains clouds and moisture.

■ **trunnion**

a pair of short journals supported in bearings projecting coaxially from opposite sides of a component required to pivot about their axis.

■ **truss**

1. a major supporting structure usually timber for roof decks.
2. a frame or jointed structure designed to act as a beam of long span, while each member is usually subjected to longitudinal stress only, either tension or compression.

■ **tuck pointing**

1. the filling in with fresh mortar of cut-out or defective mortar joints in masonry.
2. the re-grouting of defective mortar joints in a masonry or brick wall.

■ **tuned mass damper**

a mechanical counterweight designed to reduce the effects of motion, such as the swaying of a skyscraper in the wind or in an earthquake.

■ **tunnel boring machine (TBM)**

a mechanical device that tunnels through the ground

■ **tunnel shield**

a cylinder pushed ahead of tunneling equipment to provide advance support for the tunnel roof;

used when tunneling in soft or unstable ground.

■ **turbine**

a propeller or wheel device driven by the pressure of liquid or gas.

■ **turbulence**

a condition where fluid moves in random paths rather than in parallel layers.

■ **turpentine**

a volatile oil used as a thinner in paints and as a solvent in varnishes. Chemically, it is a mixture of trepans.

■ **two coat seal**

a seal coat consisting of two successive application. Refer spray seal reference chart.

■ **two-way valve**

a control valve with only two flow paths.

■ **type h asphalt**

high quality asphalt for use in wearing course in lightly trafficked areas similar to type n but is used where increased durability is required.

■ **type n asphalt**

normal duty asphalt for base, intermediate and wearing courses, ranging in size from 3 mm to 40 mm.

■ **type r**

asphalt with a high rich bitumen content used as a fatigue resistant base layer.

■ **type t**

asphalt used as a base, intermediate or wearing course in moderate to heavily trafficked areas.

■ **type v**

asphalt normally used at heavily trafficked intersections as the wearing course. High void content.

■ **ullage**

the volume of fluid, which a vessel lacks from being full.

■ **ultimate analysis**

the determination of the percentages of carbon, hydrogen, nitrogen, sulphur, chlorine and (by difference) oxygen in the gaseous products and ash after the complete combustion of an organic material of a sample.

■ **ultimate elongation**

the amount a material stretches during tensile testing before it ruptures. Usually expressed as a percentage of the original length.

■ **ultimate elongation**

in a tensile test, the elongation of a rupture

■ **ultrasonic**

a vibration with a frequency higher than that normally audible to the human ear.

■ **ultraviolet (UV)**

1. situated beyond the visible spectrum, just beyond the violet end, having wavelengths shorter than wavelengths of visible light and longer than those of X-rays;
2. relating to, producing, or employing ultraviolet radiation.

■ **unbound base**

a material which has not had a binder added e.g.. cement or bitumen.

■ **unconsolidated**

incomplete.

■ **undercoat**

a coating applied prior to the finishing or top coats of a paint job. It may be the first of two or the second of three coats. In some usage of the word it may, become synonymous with priming coat.

■ **underdrain filter**

a method of conveying groundwater away from behind a wall or abutment through the use of a porous medium and weep holes.

■ **underground storage tank**

any one or combination of underground tanks and any connecting underground pipes used to contain an accumulation of regulated substances, the volume of, which, including the volume of the connecting underground pipes, is 10 percent or more beneath the surface of the ground.

■ **underlayment**

an asphalt-saturated felt or other sheet material (may be self-adhering) installed between the roof deck and the roof system, usually used in a steep-slope roof construction. Underlayment is primarily used to separate the roof covering from the roof deck, to shed water, and to provide secondary weather protection for the roof area of the building.

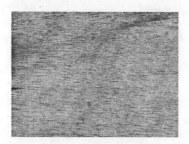

■ **unit cell**

the basic structural unit of a crystal structure.

■ **unload**

to release flow to the reservoir.

■ **unloading valve**

a valve, which by-passes flow to the reservoir when a set pressure is maintained on its pilot port.

■ **unstable**

characteristic of a structure that collapses or deforms under a realistic load.

■ **upstation**

in the direction of increasing station values

■ **U-wingwall**

a wingwall that is parallel to the feature carried.

■ **vacancy**

a normally occupied lattice site from which an atom or ion is missing.

■ **vacuum**

the absence of pressure that is, a pressure less than atmospheric. A perfect vacuum is the total absence of pressure. A partial vacuum is some condition less than atmospheric pressure.

■ **vacuum bag**

a flexible membrane used to contain the vacuum during the cure process

■ **vacuum bag moulding**

a process for moulding reinforced plastics in which a sheet of flexible transparent material such as nylon or Mylar plastics is placed over the lay-up on the mould and sealed. A vacuum is applied between the sheet and the lay-up. The entrapped air is removed by the vacuum and the part is placed in an oven or autoclave. The addition of pressure further results in higher fibre concentration and provides better adhesion between layers of sandwich construction. Also known as vacuum bagging.

■ **vacuum pressure**

a deficiency of fluid or flow resulting from too low temperature, incorrect fluid viscosity or too high suction velocity. Leads to suction difficulties and pump damage.

■ **valley**

1. a term applied to a depressed angle formed by the meeting of two inclined slopes of a roof.
2. the internal angle formed by the junction of two sloping sides of a roof.

■ **valve**

a device, which controls fluid flow direction, flow rate, or pressure.

■ **valve actuator**

the valve parts through, which force is applied to move or position flow-directing elements.

■ **valve mounting, base**

a mounting plate for a has top and side ports.

■ **valve mounting, line**

valve is mounted directly to system lines.

■ **valve mounting, manifold**

valve is mounted to a plate, which provides multiple connection ports for two or more valves.

■ **valve mounting, sub-plate**

valve is mounted to a plate, which provides straight-through top and bottom ports.

■ **valve, detent position**

a predetermined position maintained by a holding force acting on the flow-directing elements of a directional control valve.

■ **valve, open centre**

a directional control valve in, which all ports are connected to the tank line when the valve is in the neutral position.

■ **valve, prefill**

see **prefill valve.**

■ **valve, priority**

a valve, which directs flow to one operating circuit at a fixed rate and directs excess flow to another operating circuit.

■ **valve, proportioning**

this valve is a fixed differential pressure reducing valve and has a fixed spring and a fixed differential area. It is used in brake systems to limit the magnitude of the pressure to the rear brakes.

■ **valve, reducing**

this valve can produce a constant reduced pressure to a circuit downstream of the valve irrespective of input pressure.

■ **valve, spring-centred**

a valve, which is normally held in the centre position by a spring until it is moved from this position by some external force.

■ **valve, spring-offset**

a valve, which is normally held in one of its end positions by a spring until it is moved from this position by some external force.

■ **valve, three-position**

a directional control valve, which has three possible choices of flow direction.

■ Van der Waals bond

a secondary interatomic bond between adjacent molecular dipoles, which may be permanent or induced.

■ vaporisation

the change of a substance from a liquid or solid state to the gaseous state.

■ vapour

the word vapour is frequently used to describe a substance, which, though now in a gaseous phase, generally exists as a solid or liquid at room temperature.

■ vapour barrier

material used to retard the movement of water vapour into walls and prevent condensation in them. Usually considered as having a perm value of less than 1.0. Applied separately over the warm side of exposed walls or as a part of blanket insulation.

■ vapour retarder

will function to limit moisture diffusion through the veneer system. The vapour retarder is commonly placed on the interior or 'warm in winter' side of the steel stud wall, but its location may vary depending on local practice and the configuration of wall insulation used. A vapour retarder commonly contains points where minor leakage can occur, such as electrical outlets or joints at structural members, but in general these systems still function adequately. The vapour retarder can be provided as a part of the insulation backing, on the surface of the gypsum wallboard or as a separate polyethylene sheet.

■ varnish

a thickened preparation of drying oil or drying oil and resin suitable for spreading on surfaces to form continuous, transparent coatings, or for mixing with pigments to make enamels.

■ vehicle

the liquid portion of a finishing material; it consists of the binder (non-volatile) and volatile thinners.

■ veining

the characteristic lines or 'stretch marks' which develop during the aging process of soft bitumens.

■ velocity

linear or rotary speed expressed as a unit of length or angular displacement per given time.

■ **vena contracta**

the region of smallest cross section in a fluid stream. As fluid emerges from an orifice, it tends to contract in cross section reaching a minimum and then expanding back to fill the conduit.

■ **veneer**

1. thin sheet of a material, such as a layer of wood of superior value or excellent grain to be glued to an inferior looking wood b: any of the thin layers bonded together to form plywood
2. protective or ornamental facing, such as of brick or stone; in masonry: a single wythe of masonry for facing purposes, not structurally bonded.
3. a superficial or deceptively attractive appearance, display, or effect: gloss, facade.
4. a wall having a facing of masonry units, or other weather-resisting, non-combustible materials, securely attached to the backing, but not so bonded as to intentionally exert common action under load. A brick veneer wall consists of an exterior wythe of brick isolated from the backup by a minimum prescribed air space and attached to the backup with corrosion-resistant metal ties.
5. the international masonry institute 'a single facing wythe of masonry units or similar materials securely attached to a wall for the purpose of providing ornamentation, protection, insulation, etc. But not so bonded or attached as to be considered as exerting common reaction under load.'

6. veneer is non structural facing of brick, concrete, stone, tile, metal, plastic or other similar approved material attached to a backing for the purpose of ornamentation, protection or insulation. Anchored veneer is veneer secured to and supported by approved connectors attached to an approved backing.

■ **vent**

the release of pressure to actuate a balanced spool; or a small valve to allow the removal of air. Usually connected to the atmosphere.

■ **vent pipe**

a vertical pipe of relatively small dimensions which protrudes through a roof to provide for the ventilation of gasses.

■ **ventilator**

device installed on the roof for the purpose of ventilating the interior of the building.

■ **venting**

1. the process of installing roof vents in a roof assembly to relieve vapour pressure.
2. the process of water in the insulation course of the roof assem-

bly evaporating and exiting via the roof vents.

■ **venturi**

a local contraction in a conduit, which is shaped so that the loss of pressure due to friction is reduced to a minimum.

■ **vermiculite**

1. a mineral closely related to mica, with the faculty of expanding on heating to form lightweight material with insulation quality. Used as bulk insulation and also as aggregate in insulating and acoustical plaster and in insulating concrete floors.
2. an aggregate somewhat similar to perlite that is used as an aggregate in lightweight roof decks and deck fills. It is formed from mica, a hydrous silicate.

■ **vertical application**

roll roofing laid parallel to the slope of a roof.

■ **vertical clearance**

the minimum vertical distance between the bottom of the structure and the surface of the feature crossed.

■ **vested water right**

the right granted by a state water agency to use either surface or ground water.

■ **virgin flow**

the streamflow, which exists or would exist if man had not modified the conditions on or along the stream or in the drainage basin.

■ **virtual eccentricity**

the eccentricity of a resultant axial load required to produce axial and bending stresses equivalent to those produced by applied axial loads and moments. It is normally found by dividing the moment at a section by the summation of axial loads occurring at that section.

■ **virtual laboratory**

a virtual location in, which systems can be represented and simulation tests can be conducted by a human operator with visual and audible animation generated by a computer program as though the test is physically being carried out in an actual laboratory.

■ **viscoelasticity**

a type of deformation exhibiting the mechanical characteristics of viscous flow and elastic deformation.

■ **viscosity**

1. a measure of the consistency of resistance to flow of a material, normally specified for bitumen by class i.e. Class 320.
2. the internal frictional resistance offered by a fluid to change of shape or to the relative motion or flow of its parts.

■ **viscosity index**

a measure of the viscosity-temperature characteristics of a fluid compared to two arbitrary reference fluids.

■ **viscosity, absolute or dynamic**

the resistance of a fluid to relative motion of its molecules. Common units are Poise (metric), pounds per foot-second (lb/ft-sec) and Reyn in the British system of units expressed in pound seconds per square foot.

■ **viscosity, kinematic**

the ratio of absolute viscosity to the density of the fluid. It is measured in stokes in the metric system where one stoke is one centimetre squared per second.

■ **viscous lock**

a viscosity induced drag on adjacent surfaces and ultimate lockup.

■ **vitrification**

the condition resulting when kiln temperatures are sufficient to fuse grains and close pores of a clay product, making the mass impervious.

■ **void**

an open space or break in consistency.

■ **void-free density**

refer maximum theoretical density.

■ **volatile organic compounds (VOCs)**

VOCs are made as secondary petrochemicals They include light alcohols, acetone, trichloroethylene, percholoroethylene, dichloroethylene, benzene, vinyl chloride, toluene, and methylene chloride. These potentially toxic chemicals are used as solvents, degreasers, paints, thinners, and fuels. Because of their volatile nature, they readily evaporate into the air, increasing the potential exposure to humans. Due to their low water solubility, environmental persistence, and widespread industrial use, they are commonly found in soil and ground water.

■ **volatile thinner**

a liquid that evaporates readily and is used to thin or reduce the consistency of finishes without altering the relative volumes of pigment and non-volatile vehicles.

■ **volatility**

readiness of a liquid to evaporate.

■ **volcanic water**

Juvenile water (new water) furnished by lava flows and volcanic activity.

■ **volume**

the size of a space or chamber in cubic units.

■ **vulcanisation**

non-reversible chemical reaction involving sulphur or other suitable agent wherein cross-links are formed between molecular chains in rubber materials.

■ **wadding**

a loose coherent mass of fibre in sheet or lap form.

■ **waffle core**

a type of sandwich construction containing a deep drawn third sheet which acts as a core to separate and hold the two face sheets in position.

■ **wale**

a horizontal beam that runs along the inside of the walls of an excavation or cofferdam which can be braced or tied back .also known as, waler.

■ **walkways**

designated areas for foot traffic on roofs.

■ **wall plate**

a horizontal member anchored to a masonry wall to which other structural elements may be attached. Also called head plate.

PT-1 at coaxial wall plate

■ **wall tie**

a bonder or metal piece which connects wythes of masonry to each other or in other materials.

■ **wall tie, cavity**

a rigid, corrosion-resistant metal tie which bonds two wythes of a cavity wall. It is usually steel, 3/16 inches in diameter and formed in a 'z' shape or a rectangle.

■ **wall tie, veneer**

a strip or piece of metal used to tie a facing veneer to the backing.

■ **walt**

a unit of powder indicating the rate at, which work is done. The faster an agent can do work the more powerful it is, therefore, the higher its wattage.

■ **wane**

bark, or lack of wood from any cause, on edge or corner of a piece of wood.

■ **waste heat**

heat that escapes to the atmosphere during combustion processes. Minimising and recapturing waste heat is a valuable energy conserving strategy. For example, in homes there is heat in graywater, flues from wood-burning stoves, and heat pump fluids that can be captured for other uses such as preheating domestic hot water.

■ **waste water**

water for which disposal is more economical than use at the time and point of its occurrence. Waste water to one user may be a desirable supply to the same or another user at a different location. It may be waste water because of its quality, quantity, or the time of its occurrence.

■ **water**

the liquid that descends from the clouds as rain; forms streams, lakes, and seas, and is a major constituent of all living matter; is an odourless, tasteless, colourless, very slightly compressible liquid.

■ **water conserving irrigation system**

drip irrigation, soaker hoses, bubblers, and low-trajectory spray heads for water distribution; zoning irrigation for different water-demand plant types; electronic timers with five-day programming and rain override devices; irrigation schedules for early morning watering every five to seven days; soil moisture sensors.

■ **water cycle**

the process by which water travels in a sequence from the air (condensation) to the earth (precipitation) and returns to the atmosphere (evaporation). It is also referred to as the hydrologic cycle.

■ **water flow**

the rate of flow of water measured in volume and time.

■ **water hammer**

the vibration of a conduit in a fluid system due to rapid changes in liquid velocity due to valve closure.

■ **water law**

a law that has been instigated to control the right to the use of water.

■ **water level**

the water surface elevation of a particular water body.

■ **water losses**

water, which is unavailable or lost from a particular containment system.

■ **water pollution**

industrial and institutional wastes, and other harmful or objectionable material in sufficient quantities to result in a measurable degradation of the water quality.

■ **water proofing**

1. barrier which prevents the flow or passage of moisture through porous materials (masonry, concrete, etc.) due to water pressure. It can be successfully designed for either below or above grade construction.
2. the process where a building component is made totally resistant to the passage of water and/or water vapour.

■ **water quality**

a term used to describe the chemical, physical, and biological characteristics of water with respect to its suitability for a particular use.

■ **water quality standard**

a plan for water quality management containing four major elements: water use criteria to protect uses implementation plans and enforcement plans. An anti-degradation statement is sometimes prepared to protect existing high quality waters.

■ **water retentivity**

that property of a mortar which prevents the rapid loss of water to masonry units of high suction. It prevents bleeding or water gain when mortar is in contact with relatively impervious units.

■ **water spreading**

the retention of water behind dams or in basins; maintenance of flow in ditches or stream channels, or infusion of water into wells and shafts to develop influent seepage.

■ **water stop**

a device designed to protect the exposed edge of a partially installed burm from water entrance.

■ **water supply**

any quantity of available water.

■ **water supply system**

the system for the collection, storage, treatment and distribution of potable or other kinds of water from the sources of supply to the consumer.

■ **water surface elevation**

the distance the water surface in a creek or bayou is above the aver-

age sea level at a given location along the creek or bayou.

■ **water table**

a projection of lower masonry on the outside of the wall slightly above the ground. Often a damp course is placed at the level of the water table to prevent upward penetration of ground water

■ **water vapour**

moisture existing as a gas in air.

■ **water well report**

a report, which a water well contractor or landowner who is constructing his own well submits to a water resources department. It includes the location and dimensions of the well, its flow, a record of geologic materials encountered in drilling, the temperature of the ground water, and other data.

■ **water wheel**

a device such as an turbine or similar engine to transform the energy of flowing water into mechanical power.

■ **water witch**

a person who predicts the presence of underground water with hand-held tools such as forked twigs or metal rods.

■ **waterfall**

a sudden, nearly vertical drop in a stream, as it flows over rock.

■ **waterproof**

the quality of a membrane, membrane material, or other component to prevent water entry.

■ **waterproofing**

treatment of a surface or

structure to prevent the passage of water under hydrostatic pressure.

■ **water-repellent preservative**

a liquid designed to penetrate into wood and impart water repellence and a moderate preservative protection. It is used for millwork, such as sash and frames, and is usually applied by dipping.

■ **watershed**

the area of land that contributes surface runoff to a given point in a drainage system.

■ **wave**

a regular movement on a surface or within a material when energy travels through it. On the surface of an ocean or body of water, it is usually in the form of a curving swell or ridge.

■ **wave machine**

a device used for converting the energy of ocean waves into electrical energy. It can also make waves at a water recreation site for swimming or surfing.

■ **wear ring**

an element used to prevent cylinder seals from being crushed and metal-to-metal contact from occurring by maintaining seal concentricity when side loads exist.

■ **wearing course**

that part of the pavement upon which traffic travels.

■ **wearing surface**

a sacrificial layer of material on the structural deck that serves as the riding surface of the structure.

■ **wearout**

the process of attrition, which results in an increase of the failure rate with increasing age (cycles, time, miles, events, etc., as applicable for the item).

■ **weather**

the composite condition of the near earth atmosphere, which includes barometric pressure, wind, humidity, clouds and precipitation. Weather variations over a long period create the climate.

■ **weatherstrip**

narrower or jamb-width sections of thin metal or other material to prevent infiltration of air and moisture around windows and doors. Compression weather stripping prevents air infiltration, provides tension, and acts as a counter balance.

■ **weep**

leakage defined as any non—recurring fluid

■ weep hole

a hole which allows for drainage of entrapped water from masonry structures. Openings placed in mortar joints of facing material at the level of flashing, to permit the escape of moisture. Wind, like stack effect, is a natural phenomenon. Wind increases the positive air pressure acting against a building on the windward side, and produces a negative pressure on the leeward side and on the walls parallel to the wind direction. The wind also exerts a suction on flat or low-sloped roofs and a positive pressure on the windward side of steeper-sloped roofs.

■ weepage

a minute amount of liquid leakage by a seal. It has rather arbitrary limits, but is commonly considered to be a leakage rate of less than one drop of liquid per minute.

■ weld

the joining of components together by fusing. In thermoplastics, refers to bonding together of the membrane using heat or solvents.

■ well drillers

individuals who have the equipment and ability to drill or dig wells.

■ well logs

a record that is kept during well drilling of the various formations and rock materials and the depths at, which they are encountered.

■ wet cooling

a type of cooling system, which uses the evaporation of water to help dissipate excess heat.

■ wetlands

an area (including swamp, marsh, bog, prairie pothole, or similar area) having a predominance of hydric soils that are inundated or saturated by surface or groundwater at a frequency and duration sufficient to support and that under normal circumstances supports the anaerobic condition that supports the growth and regeneration of hydrophytic vegetation. The term hydric soil means soil that, in its undrained condition, is saturated, flooded, or pended long enough during a growing season to develop an anaerobic condition that supports the growth and regeneration of hydrophytic vegetation. The term hydrophytic vegetation means a plant growing in water or a substrate that is at least periodically deficient in oxygen during a growing season as a result of excessive water content. The term wetland does not include irrigated acreage used as farmland; a man-made wetland of less than one acre; or a man-made wetland not constructed with wetland creation as a stated objective, including but not limited to an impoundment made for the purpose of soil and water conservation, which has been approved or requested by soil and water conservation districts.

■ wind

moving air.

■ wind machine

a machine that generates electricity by the wind turning a generator-connected wind propeller. New models that perform at lower wind speeds are becoming available.

■ wind uplift

the force caused by the deflection of wind at roof edges, roof peaks or obstructions, causing a drop in air pressure immediately above the roof surface. This force is then transmitted to the roof surface. Uplift may also occur because of the introduction of air pressure underneath the membrane and roof edges, where it can cause the membrane to balloon and pull away from the deck.

■ windwalls

these are small outside walls on a building set perpendicular to an exterior wall with windows on the side of the wingwall. A negative pressure zone is created by the wingwalls stimulating air movement through the windows.

■ wire drawing

the erosion of a valve seat under high velocity flow conditions whereby vaporous cavitation of entrained water creates thin wire-like gullies.

■ wobble plate

a rotating canted plate in an axial type piston pump, which pushes the pistons into their bores as it 'wobbles'.

■ wood

a common natural material strong in both compression and tension.

■ wood rays

strips of cells extending radially within a tree and varying in height from a few cells in some species to 4 inches or more in oak. The rays serve primarily to store food and to transport it horizontally in the tree.

■ work

the exertion of a force over a finite distance. A measure of the energy consumed in units of force multiplied by distance.

■ work cycle

a series of load applications carried out over a prescribed distance or period of time that recurs regularly.

■ work plan

a document outlining the proposed scope of work, including a time schedule and cost expenditures.

■ work to tight fitting tolerances

skilled trade-persons are often called upon to assemble, produce and repair components to close tolerances. This mean that they have to work to a specified size and make the components as stated in the drawing of the part. If parts are not made to close tolerance the clearance or lack of clearance may cause the equipment to fail prematurely.

■ **workability**

the ease with which asphalt mix can be placed.

■ **working stress design**

a method of design based on an allowable stress that is some fraction of the yield strength of the material.

■ **woven valley**

a method of valley construction in which shingles or roofing from both sides of the valley extend across the valley and are woven together by overlapping alternate courses as they are applied.

■ **wrinkle**

a raised pattern of ridges running in a random fashion in a bur.

■ **wrought iron**

an iron alloy that is less brittle than cast iron.

■ **wythe**

1. each continuous vertical section of masonry one unit in thickness. 2. the thickness of masonry separating flues in a chimney. Also called withe or tier.

■ **x, port**

this refers to a pilot signal port.

■ **xeriscape**

creative landscaping for water and energy efficiency and lower maintenance. The seven xeriscape principles are good planning and design; practical lawn areas; efficient irrigation; soil improvement; use of mulches; low water demand plants; good maintenance.

■ **xps derivatisation**

an analytical technique in which the surface organic group such as carbonyl, hydroxyl, and carboxyl are treated with selective organic reagents prior to xps analysis.

■ **X-ray emission, proton induced**

an X-ray emission spectrometer based on physics and not on chemistry. It separates the electrons from the hydrogen atom, then an accelerator drives the protons at a high speed to collide with the target or specimen. This spectrometer is capable of evaluating 72 elements simultaneously in one sample.

■ **x-ray microscopy**

the technique of examining x-rays by means of a microscope. In a variation called point projection x-ray microscopy, an enlarged image is obtained from x-rays emitted from a pinhole point source. The technique is useful for studying the structure of materials such as laminates, fibres and filaments.

■ **y, port**

Refers to a pilot signal port.

■ **yarn distortion**

in woven fabrics, an altering of the symmetrical surface appearance by shifting or sliding of warp and filling yarns.

■ **yarn filament**

a yarn composed of continuous filaments assembled with or without twist

■ yield

The quantity of water expressed either as a continuous rate of flow (cubic feet per second, etc.) or as a volume per unit of time. It can be collected for a given use, or uses, from surface or ground water sources on a watershed.

■ yield strength

the stress at which a material exhibits a specified deviation from proportionality of stress and strain.

■ Young's modulus

the ratio of a simple tension stress applied to a material to the resulting strain parallel to the tension.

■ z factor

this factor is defined by the relation $Z = PV/NRT$ and is based on the assumption that at the same reduced pressure and temperature all gases have the same compressibility factor.

■ zero crossing

in fatigue loading, zero crossing is the number of times that the load-time history crosses the zero load level, with either a positive or negative slope, as specified during a given length of history.

■ zero-lapped

a critical-centre condition where the spool land width is identical to the port width.

■ zeta rating

a contaminant abrasivity rating system that allows the Omega Life of a component to be transformed to a Zeta Life to reflect the abrasivity severity of the environmental contaminant.

■ zinc

a metal that has application considerations including high expansion-contraction rates and low-temperature restrictions

■ zinc borates

amorphous powders of indefinite composition, containing various amounts of zinc oxide and boric oxide. They are used as flame retardants, quite often in combination with antimony trioxide

■ zone of aeration

a region in the earth above the water table. Water in the zone of aeration is under atmospheric pressure and would not flow into a well.

■ zone of saturation

the space below the water table in, which all the interstices (pore spaces) are filled with water. Water in the zone of saturation is called ground water.

■ zonolite

a lightweight, insulating concrete composed of portland cement, water, and vermiculite aggregate.

Other Books on

LOTUS ILLUSTRATED DICTIONARIES

Unit No. 220, Second Floor, 4735/22,
Prakash Deep Building, Ansari Road, Daryaganj,
New Delhi- 110002, Ph.: 32903912, 23280047, 09811838000
• E-mail : lotus_press@sify.com. www.lotuspress.co.in

CPSIA information can be obtained
at www.ICGtesting.com
Printed in the USA
LVHW080605270422
717290LV00015BA/582

9 781736 121023